Chris Mitc

'quirky'

nature notes

---

50 nature notes from the

West Highland Free Press

Christopher Mitchell
Isle of Skye

Copyright © Christopher Mitchell 2010

Published by: Christopher Mitchell
Croft 3, Waterstein, Isle of Skye, IV55 8WT
www.spanglefish.com/christophermitchell

British Library Cataloguing in Publication Data
A catalogue record for this book is available from the British Library

ISBN: 978-0-9565068-0-1

Typesetting and Design by Christopher Mitchell

Illustrations and photographs: Christopher Mitchell, unless otherwise stated

Printed by: PMM Group Ltd

Front cover: detail from the author's 60th birthday cake supplied by 'Sweet Unique', Edinburgh.
With thanks to John Mitchell

To Janet

CONTENTS

Astronomical Observations Past and Present

Maths and Physics in the Natural World

Lichens and Fungi

Alien Species

The Effects of Competition

The Natural History of a Peat Bog

A Hebridean Slant on Life

Evolution and Darwin's Legacy

INTRODUCTION

Part of the fun in writing these nature notes has been uncovering nature that is often passed by. For this reason, the essays on lichens and fungi are some of my favourites. Almost anything you say about lichen is new to most people. Almost everything I've learned about fungi makes me smile!

After living in Skye for more than half a lifetime, I realise now how much I have been influenced by this environment. The sections on birds, plant and animal distribution, climate change and astronomy, all reflect this 'sense of place'.

Here, the weather rules your life like no other factor. Crofters, fishermen, outdoor guides, high-sided-van drivers, refuse collectors, B&B landladies, builders, and gardeners are all affected in a way that is difficult to appreciate unless you have lived here.

The constant threat of gales, and torrential rain and drizzle makes you acutely aware of the cues and signs that help predict the weather. On a more formal basis, I was fortunate enough to have been employed for nearly 20 years in north Skye as an auxiliary weather observer for the Met Office.

The sections on the sea and sea shore are effectively descriptions of what is on the doorstep. Wherever you are in Skye, you are never more than five miles from the coast.

The section on maths and physics is really something I have been dragged into. I feel more at home in the biological or 'inexact sciences'. But the venture has enabled me to make sense of many puzzles. Why, for example, do plants have leaves and flowers that follow the Fibonacci sequence, and why, after a spell of warm settled weather, do I see Benbecula and North Uist as a mirage, suspended upside down in the sky?

The penultimate section contains essays that are more personal in outlook. Here, I have taken the opportunity to grumble about life's little irritations – like the size of modern tennis rackets, and why is it that everyone these days seems to be in need of a walking pole? It is a warning to the naturalist, including this one, of the dangers in taking yourself and your subject matter too seriously.

The final section deals with evolutionary concepts at the heart of modern biology. Competition and the struggle for survival does not always make pleasant viewing, and observing such behaviour first-hand keeps the sentiments in balance. When you have seen stoats and otters kill their prey, you avoid giving them Christian names.

These essays first appeared in my fortnightly nature notes column in the *West Highland Free Press*. There have been some corrections and alterations but most are as they first appeared. I thank the editor, Ian McCormack, for giving me the opportunity to write them.

I am especially indebted to Robert Arnold for his invaluable help with the computer and for suggesting many of the topics. Thanks must also go to John Roberts for his fungal forays, Geoff Collins for his gardening anecdotes, Marcus Ridsdill Smith for supplying information on the Skye moles, and to members of the Scottish Wildlife Trust (Skye Members' Centre) for sharing their expertise and local knowledge.

Perhaps the greatest input has been from my wife, Janet. It is thanks to her humour and gentle asides [mostly in brackets] that things have been kept in their proper perspective.

Strictly for the Birds

HOW TO SURVIVE THE MIDGE SEASON

Make the most of those still summer days:
find an exposed headland and study the seabirds

Midges! Here they are again. I keep telling myself it's all psychological. If you know they are about, then anything touching your skin is interpreted as a biting midge. Just a hair brushing your forehead – and it's a bite. A blade of grass brushing your hand and it's a bite. So you need to keep telling yourself they aren't really there. It's all in the mind. Like yoga, just keep repeating the mantra: 'They aren't really there'… Only they are!

Traditionally, July is the start of the midge season. If you want to escape being eaten alive then my advice is to avoid going out early morning or in the evening or any time during the daytime when it's dull or drizzly. Avoid stacking peat or picking gooseberries, or any gardening in long grass. Stay away from woodland and freshwater – and whatever you do, don't go anywhere near bracken.

With careful planning, however, you can find places to walk that are relatively midge-free, even in the west of Scotland. The secret force that grounds a midge is wind speed. Anything above 5mph and they won't fly. So the place to head for is the coast. Choose a sea cliff – any sea cliff will do – anywhere where there is an onshore breeze. The sea surface has been calm for a while now, and this is the perfect time for watching whales, sharks and sea birds.

On an exposed, rocky coastline, the first bird to catch the eye is the one flying low over the water – all black with a long neck. This is the unfortunately-named 'shag'. In more-sheltered genteel quarters, it is more likely to be named a 'cormorant' (even if it isn't). The Latin name really excels itself: *Phalocrocorax aristotelis*. The same bird is known as a 'scaw' in Norwegian, 'skarfur' in Icelandic, and 'scairbh' in Gaelic.

But how do you tell the difference between a shag and a cormorant, especially at a distance? Well, the first thing you *don't* do is spend time following a bird book! It will give you a list of morphological differences: 'The shag is smaller; is iridescent green-black instead of a duller blue-

9

black; has a yellow gape instead of a white cheek and thigh patch; sports a tuft of feathers on the forehead instead of a smooth flat profile.' And then, to remove any doubt: 'A shag has twelve tail feathers whilst a cormorant has fourteen.'

Leave the bird book to one side and just watch the way these birds fly. If it's keeping to a height of only two feet above the water, then the chances are it's a shag. If you see it flying higher or even flying steeply upwards over land, then it's a cormorant. To get into the next bay, a shag will hug the surface of the sea even if it means taking the long way round. A cormorant can take a more-direct route, overland if necessary, by flying high.

During the Second World War, a number of supply planes were loaded to maximum capacity. Many of them crashed at the end of the runway. The planes were able to get airborne but could not gain any extra height. The problem stemmed from an aerodynamic property known as the 'ground effect', which causes a wing to behave more efficiently when travelling close to the ground. Could this be the reason why shags fly low? Their wings may be so overloaded that the only way they can keep airborne is to make use of the ground effect.

You are now approaching a cliff with a variety of different seabirds. Identification becomes a process of elimination. The height the bird flies is the first clue – then the way it flaps its wings. You are standing 20 metres above sea level. Above you is a bird with loosely-flapping wings – it's either a herring gull or a great black-backed. Level with you is a stocky bird with stiff narrow wings that flap-flap-flap and then glide – it's a fulmar. Below you and close to the sea surface is a delicate bird, with a pronounced downbeat of the wing – a kittiwake. Three distinct levels of air space occupied by three different sets of birds. I'm talking too fast – it's time to stop and have a drink of tea and a Mars bar!

Whilst scanning the open sea for birds, there is a chance of spotting a minke whale. The first sighting is the hardest but once you are locked on, it can be followed more easily. It surfaces two or three times with its huge curved back and dorsal fin sliding under before disappearing for perhaps three or four minutes, only to resurface somewhere 200 metres away. On a still day like today, it is the 'blow' that alerts you first. The whale is a warm-blooded animal, and just as our warm breath condenses when it hits a cold surface, the same happens with a whale. The blow is not the whale blowing a fountain of seawater into the air as seen on old etchings of

Moby-Dick; the blow is the whale's saturated breath condensing into a vertical vapour cloud. If you are near it, you'll smell it.

The key to spotting whales is having a flat calm sea and patience to watch a particular stretch of water with something like 8x30 binoculars. You don't need a high magnification. But you do need to hold them steady and have a wide field of view to scan a large area. Sit still for half an hour on your vantage point and scan the smooth silver patches of sea for black fins. They are out there now in the Minch.

Look closer. Down in the bay below ... two fins separated by a distance of five metres: a tail fin moving lazily from side to side and a triangular dorsal fin occasionally flopping over under its own weight, giving the impression of two separate animals – a basking shark. The top of its open mouth is another five metres further forward, making a total length of ten metres – the length of a house.

This huge specimen is a female, weighing over seven tons, and has probably taken 20 years to reach this size. It is the largest species of fish to be found in our coastal waters and is harmless, unless you happen to be plankton.

As the wind drops and the sea goes flat calm you will have perfect conditions for whale and shark spotting. But there is a price to pay. Midges become active when the wind drops below 5mph. The secret is to create your own wind speed by moving faster than 5mph. This is no time to be standing still ... If you must pour a hot drink from the thermos and then finish off that cheese and tomato sandwich – it can be done ... but I can think of better things to do than leaping around my rucksack like a tethered goat.

A CASE OF MISTAKEN IDENTITY

What happened when the thrush met the 'wilk',
and the stickleback saw the Post Office van?

Last week we had B&B guests from Italy. Janet had taken the email booking: twin bedroom, mother and daughter, foreign names, omnivores.

"Can I help you with your luggage?" I ask, falling over myself to get to the car.

"Thank you," they reply in that wonderful Italian accent that sounds like the sea caressing the sands of Sorrento. Ahhh!... Sorrento.

And then, after they had settled in, I enter the sitting room with a flourish – like a fawning Basil Fawlty – to tell them with a broad joking smile that we have even arranged the calendar to make them feel at home. And I point with a grin to 'July' and the picture of Venice.

Actually, I did nothing of the kind, which was a good job, since Janet returned to the kitchen before I had chance to set off, and said: "They're from Mexico, actually."

Life is complicated enough for us humans but even the 'lower creatures' with their seemingly foolproof innate behaviour can get it wrong …

It all began in June. I was weeding the salad bed when I heard a tap-tap-tap coming from under the spruce trees.

"A thrush!" I thought to myself in total confidence.

Janet heard the same noise coming from the same place a few days later. I explained to her how a thrush was able to break open a snail's shell by picking it up with its beak and cracking it down on a chosen stone or 'anvil'. We heard it intermittently throughout most of June and July and then suddenly it stopped. No more snails?

But then I realised that it couldn't be snails because our garden doesn't have large snails. We have acid soil and so we get slugs. If we were on the limestone of Strath Suardal or in the ancient hazelwoods of Tokavaig, then it would be different. There you would find the large yellow-banded snail so beloved of the thrush. Snails need lots of calcium to make their shells. Our garden doesn't have it.

And yet the thrush was tapping away at something. I looked carefully below the spruce amongst the ever-encroaching ground elder (bloomin' Romans) and guess what? There, by a flat stone I found a pile of snails and a broken shell. But now comes the point of this story. The snails were 'wilks'!

Some years ago, we had been down to the shore and gathered a bag of wilks to eat, which we did after boiling them for ten minutes, and then easing them out with a skewer and then pickling them in vinegar, and – contrary to what you might think – they were delicious when eaten quickly with plenty of bread and butter.

We threw the empty shells out into the garden, under the spruce. But the point of the story is that the shell that the thrush had cracked open was a wilk – what biologists insist on calling *Littorina littorea* – with a shell that is over two millimetres thick towards the apex and nowhere less than one millimetre around the rim. This wasn't some weak-bellied garden snail – all stripes and no strength – this was a snail in armour.

I found a shell that had been cracked open. The thrush must have been working on it for weeks. And for what? After all that tapping through June and July, after continuously slamming down that wilk onto its anvil with a force of what must have been at least seven kilonewtons – the cupboard was bare.

No wonder the tapping suddenly stopped. But what a grave error by the thrush! All that energy and time expended when it could have been looking for worms to feed its young. What drove it to persist in such a fruitless task? How could nature allow such a fundamental mistake?

The answer, of course, is that the thrush is *thick*. It just doesn't think. It sees an object with a spiral shape about an inch long and it can't resist picking it up and smashing it down. It's what biologists call an 'innate' or inborn response. Ethologists and psychologists use the terms 'supernormal stimuli' and 'innate releasing mechanisms' or IRMs for short. It means that the thrush is thick.

Examples abound in the animal world. Pipits can't resist forcing food down a gaping mouth, even if that mouth belongs to a cuckoo and is four times its proper size. Herring gull chicks will peck at the red spot on the end of its parent's beak to get it to regurgitate food. They will also peck at a red pencil that has white bands taped around its end, sometimes preferring it to its parent's beak, even though the pencil doesn't regurgitate any food at all. Male red-bellied sticklebacks will attack the side of their glass aquarium at three o'clock each weekday afternoon because that is when the red Post Office van appears and they see the red image and can't help thinking it's a rival male.

Of course instincts can be modified with time. The thrush stopped tapping in the end, but it took two months. Not so bright after all. Not like us humans…

Italian ladies indeed!

WATCHING THE GRASS GROW

*A satirical view of birdwatching that values the glamorous over
the mundane, and why we should take a closer look at grass*

Janet tells me she was once pushing her bicycle up the hill when she saw a
man standing in the passing place by his car. He was looking intensely
through binoculars at a bird flying above.

"Buzzard!" she said with a smile as she passed by – without even looking
at the bird. The man promptly threw his field guide into the open boot,
slammed the door shut and drove away.

Now this story can be told in different ways depending on what you
want to take from it...

I like to picture an unassuming lady wearing a head-scarf (she always
wears a head-scarf when cycling), with knitting needles sticking out from
the back of the panniers (she always took knitting to work for something
to do in the lunch break).

I like to think of the man dressed in the latest outdoor gear, holding a
pair of Leitz 'trinovid' binoculars. The car is a new BMW. I have no
evidence for this, but it works better for me to imagine it this way. I also
like to think she should have poked him with a knitting needle as she
passed him by, but I suppose that would have been too direct. Far better
the verbal poke.

But then she tells me that she didn't mean to annoy the chap. She knew
that he was wanting to see an eagle and she knew that it was a buzzard.
You can, after all, tell it's a buzzard by its call.

So what is the point of this story? It reflects a deep truth about the way
we look at wildlife. An eagle is worth more than a buzzard (a bit like in
chess where a rook is worth more than a knight). But why do we favour
some species more than others?

If I am honest, I am as guilty as any 'BMW-man' ...

I took a group of keen birdwatchers out the other week to look for an
eagle. We had barely set off down the road when I happened to mention a
flock of twite (*Acanthis flavirostris*) calling in the fields alongside.

"Twite?" they exclaimed in unison. "Where?"

"Well, they're somewhere over there," I said, casually waving towards
a line of fence wire. "They're just twite. They're all over the place."

"But twite are getting really scarce," they said. "I've never seen one before."

For readers who are understandably at a loss here, I should point out that twite are one of the most boring-looking birds imaginable – birdwatchers lump them alongside pipits and dunnocks as 'little brown jobs'.

Personally, I would rather collect stamps.

Janet has just told me I ought to be more tolerant and should get out more. But then I tell her it's only natural to be attracted to the glamorous species – the eagles, the peregrines, the dragonflies and orchids. We are all guilty of ignoring those animals that are drab and plants that don't have pretty flowers.

Twite

I met someone the other day who was interested in grass. Who could be interested in grass, I thought? It's what you feed to sheep isn't it? And it always needs cutting. It's not the kind of thing to set the pulse racing or make you dive for the camera.

But perhaps it's time to give grass a chance ... Take a look at the moorland just now. Ignore all the flowers: the heathers, the eyebright and the gaudy-coloured scabious. Focus on what you have trampled-over for the past 15 years.

If it's where you've been cutting peats, the chances are you will be standing on deer grass, *Trichophorum cespitosum*. Its specific Latin name suggests that it grows in a cesspit , although someone once suggested that caespitose means 'tufted'. It's not really a grass at all. It's a sedge. Sedges have edges – take a stem and rotate it between your fingers. You can feel the edges. This is the plant that gives the moor its bright yellow-green appearance in spring, glossy green in summer, chestnut-brown in autumn, becoming mottled and straggly in winter.

Now cross over to that raised patch of drier ground. The darker deer sedge gives way to the bleached-white wiry stems of matt grass, *Nardus stricta*. If you go out just before it gets dark and look at the moor, out of the corner of your eye, the light from these white patches will reach the side of the retina and make the ground appear as if lit by torch-light.

These plants have something to say. Deer sedge tells you where to cut peat. Matt grass can tell you where the ground is dry from hidden stones. It can be used to find ancient walls and cairns. Who needs all that fancy geophysics equipment used on 'Time Team'? I remember standing in the middle of a Bronze Age cairnfield. Everything was overgrown and no sign of the hidden stones, until that is, we stopped looking for stones and focused on the vegetation. All around were discrete patches of matt grass, scattered amongst the deer sedge like pale islands in a sea of brown.

And then there are the rushes, most often represented by patches of soft rush, *Juncus effusus*. The cylindrical stems are pliable when wet and become set in the direction of the wind when they dry out. Follow any glen into the hills and notice how the rushes bend as you gain height. Sometimes you come across an area where the stems bend in a new direction, where the prevailing wind has bounced off a cliff or steep side-wall, like a billiard ball bouncing off a cushion.

Grass grows differently where there are thistles. Thistles are biennial and during their two years of growth they stop the sheep from grazing close to their spiky leaves. Strangely, this effect can carry over into a third year. You often find patches of tall grass in a thistle field grazed by sheep. The tall grass indicates first- and second-year thistles as well as third-year sites where thistles once grew. Now that's an interesting puzzle!

I must end here... just remembered I have a lawn to cut. Bloomin' grass!

MANX SHEARWATER –
'THE ALBATROSS OF THE NORTH'

*A ferry journey from Mallaig to the
Small Isles in search of the Manx shearwater*

We took a trip to the Small Isles last week. Caught the ferry across to Mallaig and then to Eigg and Muck and back. If you want to see Manx shearwaters, this is the place to be – on a ferry somewhere in the region of Rum. And that's what we found – not just one or two shearwaters, but hundreds, riding the air as if on a fairground carousel.

Shearwaters do what their name suggests. They 'enjoy' scooping low between the waves. They flirt with the wind and show a true joy of flight ... Good heavens! What am I saying? I'm almost sounding like BBC's 'Springwatch'. Actually, even the most unsentimental of biologists would find it hard not to marvel at the flight of these birds.

Along with fulmar, storm petrels and albatrosses, they belong to the bird order known as tube noses. Look closely at the bill. You can't see the exit holes of the salt glands. They are covered by a tube-like sheath with an opening at the front end. It is thought this helps the bird measure its air speed (analogous to a peto tube on a modern aircraft).

What makes these birds fly so low with apparently no effort, with just an occasional flap of their wings, and hardly any drop in height, mile after mile? Surely they are defying the laws of physics? Even the mighty eagle has to flap sometimes to gain height as it seeks out a thermal or the air deflected upwards along a slope or cliff.

It is interesting to compare the shapes of these wings. A bird of prey has different design parameters compared with a bird that has to carry nothing larger than a sand eel. The eagle and the buzzard rely on powerful flapping wings to lift their prey. They need to be able to fly slowly to spot their quarry and also to land safely in difficult terrain.

The penalty for slow flight is the stall. To delay this, the bird uses a clever device that has been copied by aircraft designers. The next time you watch a buzzard or an eagle coming in to land, focus on the leading edge of the wing, at a point about one third back from the tip. Anatomically, this is equivalent to our thumb joint. It is known as the alula or the 'bastard wing'.

And so, what happens when a bird sticks out its thumb? In aerodynamic terms, the extension on the leading edge of a wing acts as a 'slot' causing the oncoming air to ripple within a narrow boundary layer over the top of the aerofoil surface. The resulting turbulent flow hugs the upper surface and so delays the stall.

At 1000 feet above sea level, it is easy to appreciate and feel the power of rising air currents. I remember having a picnic lunch near the edge of a sea cliff. The top of my thermos flask rolled away over the edge. I ran to retrieve it – but too late. Over the edge it rolled, gone for good, down to the sea below. And then, half a minute later – up it came, held stationary in the updraught, like a ping-pong ball on a fountain. A quick catch – and I was able to pour myself another cup of tea!

So much for static soaring above a cliff top. But shearwaters are down at sea level. Where do they find such lift to keep themselves aloft? As we looked out from the side of the ferry, the answer was staring us in the face; coating my camera lens with spray; thumping the steel hull; keeping us honest on our feet as we fought against the swell from a Force 7.

Waves act as miniature hills and cliffs, and the birds were using the resultant vertical air movement in a technique known as 'slope soaring'. But this isn't the whole story – the shearwater goes one step further…

These birds are built for high-speed-gliding over open water where there are few obstacles to negotiate. Their wings are shaped long and thin with pointed tips: no slots; no fear of stalling. The body is compact and streamlined – the spitfire of the sea.

Because it is built like a bullet, a shearwater can shoot itself out from a trough in the waves at an upward angle. It doesn't have to flap because its forward momentum generates enough airspeed to climb away from the sea surface through a band of air that is itself increasing in speed with height – a property known as wind shear (the nearer you are to the sea surface, the greater the friction). Even though the bird is losing ground speed, its air speed is maintained as it shoots upwards through this progressively faster-moving band of air. Once sufficient height has been gained, it glides downwind, picking up airspeed, ready once more to turn into the wind shear. The process is called dynamic soaring.

Using this technique, the shearwater repeats its circular flight path into the wind and theoretically could stay aloft indefinitely without having to flap its wings. The only nod to physics is that without some added effort, these circular flight paths will eventually drift further and further downwind. Even the shearwater can't get something for nothing.

The wandering albatross is the supreme master of dynamic soaring, enabling it to travel hundreds of miles with just a tilt and a glide of its giant wings. We aren't able to see this fabled bird with its eleven-foot-wingspan, but here, in the seas off Rum, we have its Atlantic cousin. Keep watching from the ferry. When black wings turn to white, rising and falling between the waves – there flies the Manx shearwater – 'the Albatross of the North'.

BONXIES, BOOBIES AND FOUL-MOUTHED FISH EAGLES

A humorous look at Hebridean bird names:
some real, some imaginary and some in transition

I've been watching the rugby lately and notice that the Welsh are doing rather well. And to cap it all, they've been fielding what is virtually a club side – the 'Ospreys'!

It got me thinking about bird names and their meaning. Surely an osprey is hardly the image you would associate with a rugby team? There has to be more to it than being good at catching things, even if it is with just one hand.

And so I looked-up the name in the dictionary – 'Osprey: Large bird preying on fish; derived from the Latin *ossifraga* (*os* bone; *frangere* break)'. That's more like it – nothing to do with catching trout. It's all about breaking bones!

There's more to these bird names than meets the eye. If you consider the phonetics, or the sound a name makes, there are some unexpected results. Take corncrakes. The Latin name is *Crex crex*. And what of the raven *Corvus corax*? And then there's the cuckoo, the pipit, the peewit, the twite and the wigeon, not forgetting the kittiwake. Say the name and you hear the bird.

In my more fanciful moods, I like to think that the names help tell you where the bird comes from. 'Guillemot' just has to be from down south, brought over at the time of the Norman Conquest. And there's no mistaking 'shag' as being plain-spoken Anglo-Saxon. As for 'buzzard' (said with the lips pushed fully forward) – it probably originated from somewhere in Yorkshire, most likely near Barnsley.

Some birds do just what their name tells them to do: dippers, wagtails, turnstones and shearwaters. Some are too good at what their name suggests: skua should really be spelt 'skewer'.

Some names are a real puzzle. How many oystercatchers actually catch oysters?

Some names are out-of-date. When did a herring gull last eat a herring? More likely the 'fish-and-chip gull'.

Some names are travesties. The gannet, that much-maligned metaphor for greed, has now had the added indignity of having its Latin name changed. Somebody, probably somebody in Brussels, has deemed it no longer *Sula bassana*. I mean, that name was beautiful. People would ask me what was that glistening white bird that folded its wings and plummeted like an arrow into the sea, and I would say: "That's the Solan Goose, and the Latin name is *Sula bassana* because it is found on the Bass Rock in the Firth of Forth." And I would only have to say the word *Sula* for people from Finland and Sweden to nod their heads in recognition and for their eyes to light up. And now someone in Brussels has said it no longer exists and that from now on I must call a gannet by the Latin name *Morus*. Well, I'm sorry. I'm having none of it.

Petrels are interesting. These birds have the habit of pattering their feet on the surface of the sea as they come down to feed. They give the impression they are walking on water – like St Peter – hence 'Petra' and so 'petrel'.

Some names you wouldn't trust an inch. Could you believe anything told to you by a 'smew'?

Some names like the 'black-backed gull' remind you of *Under Milk*

Wood: '... the sloeblack, slow, black, crowblack, fishingboat-bobbing sea ...'

Some names have lost their poetry. The 'saddle-back crow' is now a 'hoodie'.

Some names are rude, or pretend to be. Take the humble 'wheatear'. Bird watchers will tell you it's derived from 'white arse'. Is this really so or was it all started by someone as a practical joke? 'Ear' doesn't sound anything like 'arse'.

Some names are appropriate. A 'dunnock' could only be a boring little-brown-job. And a 'shrike' sounds like something out of a Hammer Horror as it goes about terrorising the land, seeking to impale its prey on thorns to eat later. In some parts of the world it is known as the 'butcher bird'.

Some names have trouble with pronunciation. How many times does curlew turn into 'curloo'; pochard become 'potchard'; guillemot become 'guillemo'?

Some names don't exist but ought to: *'Halitosis' albilcilla* – has to be the 'foul-mouthed' fish eagle.

And then there's *Falco subbuteo* – whose common name is the 'hobby'. (It's true, I'm not making this up!)

Some names will always have personal associations. Why is it that whenever I hear the name 'golden oriole' I think of Raymond Briggs's *Father Christmas*? And I challenge anyone not to smile when they hear the name 'blue-footed booby'.

Some names are local and are fast spreading. More and more bird-watchers outside Orkney and Shetland are calling the black guillemot a 'tystie'. And a great skua is just as likely to be called a 'bonxie' by birdwatchers from London as it is here along the Scottish coast.

But problems can arise with birders from across the Atlantic. The American robin is really a thrush. Divers suddenly become 'loons' because of their loony tunes. Buzzards become a complete puzzle. What New Yorkers call a buzzard, we call a vulture. What we call a buzzard, they call a hawk.

Here in Scotland, bird names are often associated with place names. A close study of the OS map for Skye will reveal examples from the Gaelic including *Creag an Fhithich* – the crag of the raven; *Druim nan sgarbh* – the ridge of the cormorant, and *Biod a Choltraiche* – the peak of the razorbill. There are also the Norse names: *Annishadder* – a place where eagles live; *Arnisort* – the loch of the eagle; *Ramasaig* – the bay of the raven and *Shulista* – the steading of the solan goose.

Some bird names are shrouded in mystery. 'Tiercel' is a word used in falconry to describe the male bird. It comes from the Old French name for 'third'. One explanation involves the habit of taking the falcon's third egg so as to rear it as a smaller and therefore more agile bird. But then it all gets confusing because the male falcon is naturally smaller than the female.

Perhaps there's a lesson here for modern rugby. Perhaps there's too much emphasis on size and not enough on speed and agility.

'Tiercels' v 'Ospreys'. Now that would be an interesting match!

The Sea Shore

BEWARE THE LION'S MANE!

*A close look at jellyfish from real-life encounters
to Sherlock Holmes, and why the sea turns red
during the day and glows green at night*

There is slime and there is slime. Take jellyfish for example. Most of us are wary of touching them for fear of being stung. But not all of them are dangerous. There are stingers and there are those that wouldn't hurt a fly – spending their life just floating about and quietly eating plankton.

The moon jelly (*Aurelia aurita*) is one of these. It is our most-common species and is easily identified by its four horseshoe-shaped rings on its back. The rings are the reproductive organs: the testis and ovaries, which occupy four transparent pouches or sleeves extending out from the central stomach. I've heard of wearing your heart on your sleeve, but the moon jelly takes some beating: this animal wears its balls on its sleeve.

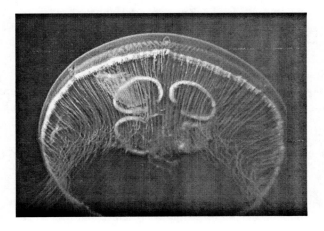

The moon jelly. The four horseshoe-shaped rings are the reproductive organs
(underwater photograph: courtesy of Robert Arnold)

The moon jelly won't harm you. It doesn't use stinging cells to catch its prey, but instead uses the sticky surface of its body to mop up plankton, moving its victims towards its mouth on a stream of slime.

But then we meet a really unpleasant character – 'the lion's mane', also known as 'the great stinger'. It is the largest-known species of jellyfish. In some parts of the world it reaches a diameter of over six feet. Here, around our own coast it averages about one and a half feet across. The real danger is in the tentacles, which often extend a staggering distance of 20 feet! They spread outwards like a giant spider's web waiting to catch their prey and paralyse it with a battery of highly-poisonous stinging cells.

The colour is usually a dark red or orange brown. Lobster fishermen know it well. Broken tentacles can sometimes become entangled in the ropes being hauled in. Painful stings carried onto the hands can be a real problem especially if you happen to touch your eyes.

A visitor was telling me how he had been swimming in LochBroom and thought he was entering a patch of seaweed when he realised it wasn't seaweed at all. The encounter left him covered in weeping pustules, unable to sleep or lie down, feeling continuously pinpricked as if covered in midge bites. The symptoms lasted for 24 hours before getting back to normal.

Conan Doyle wrote a Sherlock Holmes mystery based on such an encounter. *The Adventure of the Lion's Mane* describes the effect on the victim in lurid detail: "His back was covered with dark red lines as though he had been terribly flogged by a thin wire scourge ... there was blood dripping down his chin, for he had bitten through his lower lip in the paroxysm of his agony."

Well, that's no more swimming for me this summer.

The amazing thing about all these jellyfish is that they have grown to their full size in just one season, starting out in early spring as a miniature pulsating bell and growing to the size of a large dinner plate by mid-August – which indicates just how much food they must be eating.

The sea around the Hebrides is one of the most productive fishing grounds on the planet. Minute floating plants (phytoplankton) are eaten by small 'grazing animals' which in turn are eaten by fish. Herring fishermen knew of these links in the food chain. If the phytoplankton was scarce, that was a good sign. It meant there were lots of grazers about, which in turn would attract the herring. Experienced fishermen knew when not to fish – when the phytoplankton levels were high, they could smell it in the seawater.

Occasionally in warm weather, things get out of hand and the plankton forms huge floating mats or blooms. This frequently happens in the Red Sea – that's why it's called the Red Sea. The plankton grows so rapidly that it changes the colour of the surface water and forms red tides.

Here in Britain, we can also get red tides. Sailors crossing the Minch in summer often describe what looks like oily tomato soup floating on the surface. I well remember seeing such red patches being washed ashore in August after a spell of settled warm weather. But that wasn't the end of it, for when it got dark, the sea began to glow.

Throw a stone into such a red soup and you get a flash of light. It is caused by a dinoflagellate called *Noctiluca scintillans*. Each individual is a single cell, a gelatinous floating ball the size of a pin-head. Each sphere has a groove with a mouth and a prehensile tentacle for pushing food into the mouth. But that's not the exciting bit.

The Latin name tells you it is going to flash with light when it gets dark. And that's exactly what it does when it is physically disturbed – by a stone or a boat cutting through it, or a stick, or a dog jumping in, or if you take some in a bottle and shake it in the dark. Biologists call it bio-luminescence.

Benjamin Franklin believed it was an electric discharge involving salt, but he got it wrong. It took two Venetian naturalists in 1750 to discover that it was due to a living organism. They found *Noctiluca* emitting light in the Adriatic. It is one of the unsung wonders of the natural word – an underwater firework display – and it can happen right here on our doorstep.

And so, this summer, especially throughout August, keep a lookout on the sea surface for greasy patches resembling tomato soup. They are likely to accumulate on west-facing shores with a jetty or rocky promontory that intercepts the surface currents. And if you are out at night, sailing a boat with a toilet that pumps seawater in and out, then you could get more than you bargained for. A yachting friend of mine described how the flushed water would sparkle and flash as it disappeared down the drain hole!

Life is full of surprises.

PUT ON YOUR WELLIES FOR
A WALK ON THE SEA BED

A visit to the sea shore coincides with the year's lowest spring tide
to discover life in the west coast maerl beds

There are certain places that are out of bounds. You can't just set off across
the Sahara Desert, Antarctica, or the bottom of the sea without specialist
equipment. But when the new moon appears, it's time to put on your
wellies and get walking…

What I'm referring to is the sea bed. The only time you would expect
to walk down here is if you were a diver. But with careful planning, you
can reach places that few air-breathing mortals have seen. Buy a set of tide
tables and look for the lowest tides. Twice every 28 days, the sea goes
further out than usual. Sometimes it goes even further out than that, if the
sun and the moon are perfectly aligned.

In north Skye, we are familiar with a rocky exposed shore. The beaches
are mostly boulders and pebbles or occasionally black sand from the basalt.
The seaweeds are short, tough and have few air bladders. The anemones
retract their tentacles when touched. Bands of black lichen from the 'splash
zone', extend far up the rocky shore, indicating just how far the salt spray
is carried on the wind. And when the tide goes out, you are confronted by
a tangle of leathery kelp, slippery and dangerous to tread.

I recently visited a mainland shoreline away from the direct wave action
of the Minch. Here was a shore quite unlike any I had seen before. There
was the usual knotted wrack indicating shelter, but alongside was a peculiar
floating form of the same species locally known as 'crofters' wigs' – live,
unattached seaweed that floats and yet stays in the same place, tide after
tide. When you find this particular form you know you have extreme shelter.

Then there are the sea squirts: blobs of red jelly that squirt water at
your camera lens when someone points it out and kindly squeezes it for
you; cowrie shells that are quite difficult to spot and are known by the
amusing Latin name of *Trivia*; peacock worms that make four-inch-tall
tubes of mud and wait for the slow-moving sea to cover them before sticking
out their fan-shaped crowns; and hermit crabs, not your ordinary small
variety, but those that have grown to fill empty whelk shells the size of
goose eggs.

Was I really walking on the sea bed? Was that really an oyster; a horse mussel the size of a shoe-horn; a top shell I'd never seen before that looked like a rolled-up turban; and most exciting of all – the snakelocks anemone – shades of the Medusa or the Gorgon's head? The legend is that you will turn to stone if you look directly at it. But I think I got away with it by using the digital camera. On most rocky shores we get used to seeing the red beadlet anemone, which closes tightly when the tide is out or if disturbed. Here was a completely different beast. The snakelocks doesn't retract its tentacles.

Sea anemones have tentacles that are covered in stinging cells. They are, after all, a relative of the jellyfish. This doesn't stop them being attacked and eaten by one of the sea's most-beautiful creatures – the sea slug. These animals eat the anemone, tentacles and all, and store the stinging cells in separate sacks which they carry on their backs. They use the poison for their own defence by making themselves less palatable. Sea slugs that do this are invariably brightly coloured, which sends a clear signal to any would-be predator.

It was flat and muddy in places and my right welly was leaking, but all this was worth it. Just around the corner was a bed of maerl. Biologists refer to it as coralline seaweed but most people know it as 'coral'. I had seen it in Skye at the famous Coral Beaches of Dunvegan. It can also be found at Ord. But to appreciate it at its best you have to be out at the lowest of tides and see it alive. When alive, it's coloured purple-red. When it dies and breaks up, it turns white as it becomes bleached by the sun.

There were sea urchins that were still alive and crawling. There were giant starfish with seven arms. That can't be right. All these animals have five-sided symmetry. They should only have five arms. "Perhaps the other two are legs," someone said.

We turned around with the tide and retraced our steps into the setting sun. Hidden in the silty sand were razor shells, and as the tide approached they each squirted a jet of water vertically into the air. These fountains were reaching heights of up to three feet, sparkling in the backlight of the sun. Amazing!

The really amazing thing is that all this is on our doorstep. The seashore has been described as one of the richest habitats on the planet. You don't have to go to the Great Barrier Reef or other exotic places to see it. Snorkels and face-masks are unnecessary. All you need are some tide tables, a small handlens – and wellies that don't leak.

TRANS-ATLANTIC CROSSING TAKES
THREE YEARS AND GOES UNNOTICED

The life cycle of the European eel, and what
happened when the elver met the waterfall

We went fishing last week. The mackerel have been in since April, so I thought it was time to go down to the rocks and start catching some. It's not a sport. It's a matter of getting there, casting out, three feathers, three mackerel, hit them on the head, free the hooks, cast out again. Someone next to me was slowly going through the motions, with a single spinner. He'd catch one and then play it slowly towards him and then carefully land it and take it off the hook – and then throw it back! He was enjoying the whole experience – the scenery, the fresh air, the relaxation of being on holiday. And there was me, frantically trying to fill the freezer.

Janet came with me last time. She seems to get some relaxation from it, but then she isn't catching them. She sits up above and watches – knitting! Having caught all I can, I set to work gutting and cleaning the fish ready to take home.

There really is something perverse about your wife watching and knitting whilst you set about chopping the heads off 25 mackerel.

"How many is that?" she asks – knit-one, pearl-one, knit-two-together. Chop! Another head rolls off the block.

"This is ridiculous," I shout, "It's like watching the Guillotine during the French Revolution!"

People will come from all parts of the world to see the machair with its wildflowers. They will travel hundreds of miles to reach Balranald in North Uist to hear a corncrake. When you live in this part of Scotland, it's easy to take the scenery and wildlife for granted. But there is one particular event that stops me in my tracks every time: the sight of elvers seeking out their freshwater feeding grounds.

The eel hatches from an egg in the Sargasso Sea somewhere off the coast of Bermuda. They start life as a flat transparent larva called a leptocephalus (meaning 'thin head') which is then carried eastwards on the Gulf Stream.

Having completed a three-year journey from the Sargasso Sea, having crossed the Atlantic, single-handed, unnoticed and unannounced – they wait off shore. What are they waiting for? The chemistry of the sea to change due to the extra fresh water from heavy rain entering the rivers and pushing out into the bay? Or perhaps they are waiting for the full moon?

Before making their move, they change shape, becoming slimmer and worm like. At this stage they are known as 'glass eels' because they are transparent. You can even see the heart and gills moving inside the body.

Now they make their move ... You are not going to believe this, honest, but I saw elvers, no thicker than Janet's knitting needles, creeping up an overhanging rock face 20 feet high, behind a waterfall, clinging on by surface tension and wriggling upwards. Every now and then, one would drop down into the pool below only to start the climb all over again. Overhanging rock. Twenty feet high. Just completed a trans-Atlantic-crossing. You must be joking!

But some must make it into the river above, and then into the loch where they spend the next 15 to 20 years growing, first into a 'yellow eel' and then into a 'silver eel'. And for what? To make the return journey back over that waterfall, crashing onto that rough shore, and back to the Sargasso Sea to breed and start the whole cycle all over again. That's special!

All the European eels from the Baltic down to the Mediterranean are thought to complete this circular migration, beginning and ending in the Sargasso Sea – a particular patch of the Atlantic, near the Bahamas, 3000 miles away. Apart from anything else, it adds support to the theory of Continental Drift which explains how North America and Europe were once closer together and have since been drifting further apart. The poor old eel has had to swim that little bit further each year to make it back to its favourite breeding ground.

Strangely enough, no adult European eel has ever been caught in the area of the Sargasso Sea – they seem to disappear somewhere in the Atlantic.

I like to think the Scottish elver completed its life cycle and made it back. Some researchers believe otherwise and suggest the life cycle is completed by the American eel, which they believe to be the same species. Tagging experiments have yet to settle the issue, but as the philosopher once said – it only takes one silver eel to make a 'black swan'.

THE PRIVATE LIFE OF A LIMPET

What happens when limpets move?
How do they find their way home?

Of all the creatures on the sea shore, the limpet looks the least active. It appears permanently fixed to its spot on the rock, secure under its corrugated roof. But even limpets have to go out sometime. They need to eat and that means leaving the comforts of home and the security of their own patch.

On a low tide when it gets dark, you will find them, *en masse*, moving over the surface, munching the fine felt of algae. They sway from side to side, leaving only their teeth-marks and a trail of slime behind them.

And after a night on the town, the happy mollusc staggers back home and, amazingly, actually finds it!

How does it do that? In some experiments, the returning reveller is picked up and put down on a different street. It still makes its way home. In another experiment, a giant blob of plaster is put in its way. It manages to find its way around the edge and, after sniffing around in a circle, it unerringly returns to base. How can it do that? I can't do that. How can a limpet do that?

Some people have suggested it can memorise the route it took when it set out, somehow memorising important landmarks, like remembering to turn left out of Rose Street and then right at St Andrew's Square; or, more likely, it follows the chemical trail that it left behind on its outward journey. [I'm not going to say anything about shop doorways.]

Sometimes, down Hanover Street, the limpet gets mugged by an oyster-catcher and never makes it back home…

Meanwhile, back home, the empty site lies vacant, a lonely circle cut into the soft sedimentary rock: a scar that was ground out and excavated to fit the owner's shell perfectly. If the rock is harder than the shell, it is the shell that is worn away to fit the base exactly. On an exposed shore, this perfect fit enables the limpet to attach itself even more firmly to the rock.

The limpet's circular foot may suggest that it acts like a giant suction pad, by sealing around the edge with its sticky mucus and then pushing down flat onto a flat surface. But as well as using the whole area of its foot in this way, it can grip individual bumps and imperfections on the surface, around which it appears to form a localised vacuum. Try moving a limpet

Limpet scars

and you can feel it instantly tightening its grip.

For an oystercatcher wanting a meal, this provides quite a challenge. You sometimes find an empty limpet shell on the shore with notches chiselled into its edge. The notches are often concentrated along one particular edge, which happens to be the head-end of the limpet – where the muscle is weakest. Somehow the bird has learned to attack the weak spot. We can recognise this with practice by looking at the angle of the shell: the head lies under the steepest angle. Presumably the oyster catcher has worked this out too.

I have noticed around Skye that the majority of limpets on vertical or steeply-sloping surfaces attach themselves in a head-down position. Desiccation is a major problem for limpets on exposed shores and perhaps this orientation helps keep the vital head-end from drying out.

Some species of limpet are territorial and won't tolerate other limpets squatting on their patch. They will actually push the intruder away like a lumbering dodgem car. And then you come across a puzzle: three limpet scars that overlap. Is this just one limpet that has an itchy foot and has shuffled about to get a better grip? If so, it must have been happy in one spot for a long time to grind-out its first outline, before shifting along to take up a second position and then a third.

Limpets appear to have an internal clock and a set of tide tables. Recent research on our common limpet, *Patella vulgata*, has found two distinct periods of activity. They are either active during the day when the tide is in, or during the night when the tide is out.

But behaviour is never that simple. Limpets found on horizontal surfaces tend to be active during daylight at high water. Those occupying vertical surfaces are more active at night at low water – but only in late summer. In spring, these same denizens of vertical rock switch their behaviour and venture out at high tide in broad daylight.

Some build flat roofs and some build tall roofs. You would expect that in exposed sites with strong tidal currents, their shells would have a flatter profile. But around north Skye, the opposite is often the case. It seems that the muscular action of holding on tight causes the shell to grow into a steeper cone. Strange things these limpets.

I got a bit excited earlier, describing limpets as having a lads' night out. It could easily have been a ladies' night-out. There are males and of course there are females, only it gets a bit more complicated with limpets. They start life as males and, as they get older and larger, they change into females. It happens.

The traditionalist is at once disturbed. In a time of increasing tolerance and liberalism he seeks out the security of absolutes. But don't worry – a limpet smaller than a Polo mint is still likely to be a bloke.

Observing the Weather

WHEN THE WIND BLOWS:
A NEW BEAUFORT SCALE FOR THE HEBRIDES

*The regular occurrence of storm-force winds
shapes the lives of plants, animals and people
along Scotland's western seaboard*

After watching all those TV films over Christmas and New Year, I can't help thinking about the special effects. There is Chekov on Antares 5, kitted-out in a full space suit to counter the hostile environment. The wind is approaching 100mph, and yet he is walking normally. No space helmet ripped off. No bits of spaceship door being torn away.

Hollywood directors just don't understand the effects of wind. The noise is always that high-pitched whine that you get near telephone wires. The actors are always walking upright instead of crawling or at best walking at a 45-degree stoop. Come to the Hebrides and learn your craft – that's what I say!

Flag tree

I know it's windy in Tierra del Fuego and at the North and South Poles. And there's no denying it's difficult pitching a tent on Everest. But we're talking about people living their daily lives in almost constant wind, not just going out for a few weeks on expedition. People come to this part of Scotland on holiday: "Bloomin' windy and it's rained all week." To which I reply: "Think yourself lucky you're on holiday – we have to live here!"

And so you adapt. Plants have different shapes. Trees look like tattered flags. In fact they are technically known as 'flag trees' because of their shape. Tree trunks don't grow evenly. Logs cut from a tree that has grown in sheltered conditions will usually be round but if the tree has been exposed to winds from a particular direction, the logs will be oval. This is because more tissue is added to the sides that experience constant bending and stretching.

Wind exposure can often be gauged by observing the altitude above which trees will not grow – what botanists call the 'tree line'. In the British Isles the average tree line has been put at 2000 feet. But on some of our west-facing coasts, the tree line is at sea level. This means that many of us experience winds outside our front doors that the rest of the country would only find on a mountain top. No wonder we wait for the wind to drop before hanging out the washing.

It's easy (and natural) to exaggerate these things, especially when you have a wide-eyed audience from down south listening agog as you recall how a double mattress once appeared in the back garden: "There it was, soaked in rain – it took four of us to lift it!" And then the punchline as you describe how the wind got up again in the night and by morning the mattress had gone! But these things do happen.

The heather grows in tight cushions which is the most efficient shape to withstand the blast. Most mountain plants follow the same pattern, like moss campion, thrift, and various saxifrages. Even the seaweeds grow differently where the wind causes more turbulence. On exposed shores, bladder wrack, *Fucus vesiculosus*, has fewer floatation bladders and is known as *F. vesiculosus* var. *linearis*. The plant has adapted to the rough sea conditions. Too many bladders would result in the fronds being torn off or the whole plant being dislodged. In contrast, the delicate bladder-filled seaweed, *Ascophyllum nodusum*, is able to thrive in the more-sheltered bays.

Limpets that grow in exposed conditions have steeper sides to their shells than those found in more-sheltered conditions. This is not what you would expect. Surely in a strong turbulent flow, a shallow shell would be better? But it is thought that the extra muscular activity needed to stay attached causes the growing shell to be put under greater inward tension, which creates a taller, steeper shell.

In strong winds we are like limpets, sat under our shells as a Force 10 rages overhead. I remember the local planning authority was never happy with flat roofs and I always thought this was because they were difficult to waterproof. But perhaps a steep-sided roof performs better in a gale. Perhaps roofs in this exposed part of Scotland have 'evolved' to be like limpets.

This is pure speculation only, but if you consider a pitched roof as an aerofoil – approaching the classic shape of an aircraft wing – it will generate lift as it takes on a flatter profile. It could help explain why shallow-pitched roofs are so prone to gale damage. They act like a wing. Most slates are pulled off just behind the ridge as the wind tries to lift the roof into the air.

In the garden, it is the dwarf plants that do best: dwarf peas such as *Kelvedon Wonder* – with their thick, supporting tendrils – rather than the taller more delicate main-crop varieties. Dwarf sprouts do well in some places. Treading the ground before planting produces firmer sprouts and helps stop the plants from being torn out of the ground.

Before the invention of specialised recording equipment, wind speed was measured by looking at the effect it was having on the environment. For Sir Francis Beaufort, an admiral in the British Navy in 1805, it meant devising a scale that looked at the condition of the sea and comparing it with the speed that could be reached by a man-of-war (fighting ship). Force 3, for example, was a 'Gentle breeze' equivalent to 7 to 10 knots with the observation of 'Large wavelets... perhaps with scattered white horses.' A Force 9 was a 'Strong gale' equivalent to 41 to 47 knots when 'Crests of waves begin to topple and roll over.'

The observations were later adapted to give effects that would be experienced on land. Force 3: 'Leaves and small twigs in constant motion; wind extends light flag.' Force 9: 'Slight structural damage; chimney pots and slates removed.' I sometimes wonder what Sir Francis would have produced had he lived in this part of Britain...

Force 7: 'Moderate gale'; 32 to 38 knots; 'Sheets and towels ripped off washing line; slight inconvenience when feeding chickens.'

Force 12: 'Hurricane'; over 75 knots; 'Car doors removed; wheely-bins disappear; considerable difficulty when filling coal bucket.'

Animals adapt. Birds such as ravens and herring gulls can still fly even in speeds up to Force 10. They sweep their wings back like a modern fighter jet and hold a position almost stationary before swooping away. Astonishing!

Sheep just sit it out. Chickens just don't come out. Humans don't sleep, get annoyed at power cuts, wonder if the fire is too high and worry if the roof will still be there in the morning. Exposure to such elemental forces takes its toll. You just can't do what you want to do. You can't say that you will mend the fence tomorrow, paint the house on Saturday, or fix the chimney next week. You can only do what the wind will allow you to do... Well, that's my excuse anyway.

NINETY-NINE DIFFERENT WAYS
TO REPORT THE WEATHER

The science of weather recording and the reaction of the Romantics against analysis. An explanation of a rare reflected light rainbow

"What's the weather doing?"

April showers.

"But are they slight, moderate or heavy? Are they close-by or at a distance? Are they falling from a cloud but not reaching the ground? Is there thunder and lightning, hail, or rain and hail? And did precipitation occur in the past hour or at the time of the observation?"

Before I started reporting the weather 20 years ago, I thought that it just rained. It was quite simple. You looked outside. This stuff was coming down from the sky and you got wet. Sometimes it was 'cats-and-dogs'; sometimes it was 'bucketing-down'. But I soon found out that the Met Office required a more dispassionate report of what was actually happening.

Alright, so it's 'raining hard' as opposed to yesterday when it was 'just raining' and the day before that when it was 'still raining but not quite so hard, but still raining'.

"Sorry – still not accurate enough. There has to be a list of conditions that all weather reporters use: a standardised list that can be recognised by everyone involved in reporting the weather."

Alright, I can accept that. Can I see the list, please?

This is the moment when you find out if being an auxiliary weather observer is really the job for you. You've heard of the Inuit and how they have 20 separate names to describe 20 different types of snow – well, that's nothing to what you are about to see. Here is the list. On it there are ninety-nine different types of weather!

Take precipitation. It is classified quite precisely according to relative humidity, visibility and the size of the water droplets. If relative humidity falls below 100 per cent, fog becomes mist. As soon as visibility rises above 1000 metres, fog becomes drizzle. Increase the droplet size to 0.5 millimetres and drizzle turns to rain, except when it falls from a cumulus cloud when rain is classified as 'showers'.

This brings us to one of nature's most-spectacular events – the refraction of light in a rainbow.

The poet, John Keats didn't like the idea of scientists 'unweaving a rainbow':

> Do not all charms fly
> At the mere touch of cold philosophy?
> There was an awful rainbow once in heaven:
> We know her woof, her texture; she is given
> In the dull catalogue of common things.
> Philosophy will clip an Angel's wings,
> Conquer all mysteries by rule and line,
> Empty the haunted air, and gnomèd mine—
> Unweave a rainbow, as it erewhile made
> The tender-person'd Lamia melt into a shade.
> (*Lamia, ii. 37*)

A similar attack on analytical science appears in J.R.R. Tolkien's *The Lord of the Rings* when Gandalf denounces 'Saruman the White' for becoming 'Saruman of Many Colours':

"He that breaks a thing to find out what it is has left the path of wisdom." (*Book 2: The Council of Elrond*)

If science is to answer these criticisms it must reveal the beauty hidden within 'the dull catalogue of common things'. A rainbow can still hold its charm even when dismantled.

In fog, droplets as small as 0.05 millimetres in diameter form a white rainbow or 'fogbow'. As the droplet size increases, different colours begin to appear. In drizzle with drops of about 0.3 millimetres in diameter, the outer band turns orange and the inner bands begin to glow pink and violet. But it is not until the drops exceed 1 millimetre in diameter that the full spectrum appears – from brilliant red to intense violet.

Here in the west of Scotland we are fortunate in having some of the best rainbows anywhere in the country. Look outside on a showery day this April and the chances are you will see a 'primary bow'; violet on the inside, red outside; then a gap – not an ordinary gap but a gap of darker sky – before meeting the fainter and broader 'secondary bow', with red on the inside and violet on the outside.

Rainbows in this part of the world are often seen above water. If the surface is calm, you will see the reflections of both primary and secondary bows.

So now there are four rainbows. But that isn't the end of it. Imagine now that conditions become mirror-calm – not a breath of wind. What you are about to see really is special and extremely rare, so rare that a correspondent writing in the Royal Meteorological Society magazine, *Weather* in May 2002, reported that there were only three photographs worldwide that had captured the event!

Imagine then, standing in flat calm conditions overlooking Broadford Bay. You are facing south east; the Co-op is to your right; a shower of rain in front; late evening sun behind; digital camera poised. Four rainbows appear on cue: primary, secondary, reflected-primary, reflected-secondary. And then, sheer amazement! Another rainbow enters the picture, joined to the first primary like a giant 'tick-mark' written across the sky.

What you are witnessing is the formation of a 'reflected-light rainbow'. At a point where the ordinary rainbow strikes the water, up shoots another bow, but this bow appears almost straight with hardly any curve. The light that forms this coloured band is not coming directly from the sun above, but from the reflected sun hidden somewhere in the water below where you are standing. Magic!

The science of weather reporting draws mostly on physics, but some events involve biology. Take rainfall. Sometimes it rains fish, as happened in Aberdare in Glamorgan on the 9th February 1859 when a third of an acre was suddenly covered in minnows and sticklebacks. On the 29th May 1928, fish from the sea rained down on Comber in Ireland. Sometimes there are showers of frogs, sometimes toads and occasionally newts. The animals are carried upwards in the centre of a violent waterspout and then deposited in the downdraught around the edge of the funnel cloud.

Clouds have also been found carrying bacteria. Earlier this year, researchers found 'ice-nucleating proteins' from bacteria in snow taken from several different continents. These proteins are able to seed the clouds and so trigger the formation of snow and rain. The suggestion is that bacteria have evolved these proteins specifically to aid their dispersal.

One such bacterium, *Pseudomonas*, responsible for rotting my potatoes last year, can hitch a ride on air currents and cause water molecules in clouds to coalesce in patterns that resemble snow crystals. The resulting snowflakes and raindrops bring the bacteria back down to earth, to feed on someone else's potatoes.

Janet has just said it's looking dark outside and we need to rush out to bring in the washing. But it's OK, I tell her. It's only *Number 15* on the list – 'Precipitation within sight, reaching the ground or surface of the sea – but not at the observing station.'

Once a weather observer, always a weather observer!

CLOUD SHAPES HELP PREDICT THE WEATHER

The influence of Luke Howard in naming the clouds. Identifying the three main west coast clouds and the weather they predict

The clouds are such an everyday part of our lives that we hardly stop to notice them. Yet if we lived on Jupiter and observed Earth through a telescope, we would be in awe at the swirling white patterns.

"Look at that 'Great White Spot'," we would say, pointing to an oval disc over Skye and the Uists, "... must be 100mph winds down there." And sometimes we would be right!

Until Luke Howard devised a scientific system of names in 1802, these swirling white masses of water vapour and ice crystals were difficult to categorise. Clouds are now classified as low, medium or high depending on the height of the cloud base. They are also classified by their shape, for example – Cumulus looks like cauliflowers, Stratus forms in layers and

Cirrus is like wispy hair.

Within each group or 'genus' there are different 'species'. Cumulus congestus looks like a cauliflower that is ready to be picked whilst Cumulus humilis appears much flatter – like the clouds seen over Springfield at the start of *The Simpsons*. The list of species includes a number of distinct forms that can help us predict the weather: floccus (fluffy) – indicates warm settled spells; fractus (ragged) – indicates rain or drizzle; uncinus (with hooks) – a sign of strong high-altitude winds; lenticularis (lens-shaped) – associated with a steady airflow over mountains; and castellanus (with turrets) – a sign of violent showers developing in the afternoon during a hot humid spell.

Here in the West Highlands, there are three types of cloud we should be worried about. The first is cirrostratus – a thin veil of high-altitude ice crystals. This is the alarm bell for an approaching warm front. The warning sign is a faintly-coloured halo around the sun. If you see this in the morning, the chances are it will be raining in the afternoon.

The second is stratus. Why worry about stratus? Because it can appear on Saturday and you have a group of keen birdwatchers arriving in the afternoon staying at your B&B and they have come to watch birds and by Thursday they are getting fed up of not being able to see further than the garden gate. That's stratus.

The third is cumulonimbus. It's like cumulus but not as friendly. In fact it's foul. It brings massive hail squalls. Occasionally it brings thunder and lightning as the charged water droplets and hail stones float up and down in a column of air reaching over 30,000 feet.

How do you know there's going to be a violent squall? Look for the downdraught forming globular bulges along the base of the cloud. The main danger at this point is being struck by lightning. If you are near the house and you see these bulges beginning to form – run for cover. If you are out on the hills and you have an ice axe or are holding a metal umbrella, put them to one side. Don't shelter under a cliff where the currents could jump across the 'spark gap'. Get off the summit peak or ridge if possible and stay clear of tall isolated trees. Take up a crouched position sitting on top of your rucksack and keep your hands on your lap and away from the ground. And if you are carrying a pair of carbon-fibre walking poles with spring-loaded tungsten tips – a snip at just fifty pounds [and Janet has just kicked me in the ankle yet again] – then place them carefully to one side.

Cumulonimbus clouds often take on dramatic colours. In the early morning or late evening (when the sun is near the horizon), the lower portions often glow a bright orange or yellow with slate grey shadows in between. In contrast, the ice crystals within the upper regions reflect the full spectrum and so appear brilliant white. The top of the cloud often becomes flattened and drawn out into thin plumes by high-altitude winds. When this happens the cumulonimbus can take the form of a huge anvil.

Because of the rapidly-changing air movements within these clouds, they can be a real danger to aircraft. For this reason they are the first on the list of clouds to be reported by Met Office weather stations. I remember sending in the cloud reports from Skye: "Two 'oktas' (two eighths of the sky) covered in 'Cb9' (code for anvil-type cloud); cloud base 2000ft; visibility over 70km." That was the amazing thing. Whenever you had cumulonimbus without precipitation, the horizontal visibility was exceptionally good.

When the first *International Cloud Atlas* was published in 1896, the clouds were placed in ten separate genera and cumulonimbus was ranked as 'Cloud 9'. It is interesting to note that this description has been retained in popular language. To be 'on Cloud 9' is to be in a state of euphoria – although aviators may have a different way of putting it.

And so we find our enthusiastic weatherman with a somewhat sceptical companion, extolling his passion for storm clouds:

"Here in the West Highlands, we are fortunate in having some of the most dramatic cloud formations in Britain."

"You mean we get filthy weather."

"Don't be so pessimistic. Looking across the Minch to the Outer Isles, we have a superb uninterrupted view of an approaching cold front: magnificent cumulonimbus clouds following each other and reaching over 40,000 feet into the troposphere. The tops are drawn out into ice-filled cirrus whilst the downdraughts along the base are forming globular bulges known as 'mamma'"

"OK, you've got me interested. Why are they called mamma?"

"Because mamma is the Latin name for the female breast."

[... Prolonged silence followed by stretching of neck muscles]

DAZED MAN IN UNDERWEAR HIT BY GIANT FLAN

The realities of life on a windswept island
and the problems of forecasting the weather west of Glengarry

There are some few things that annoy me: the way that tennis players grunt whenever they hit the ball, mobile phones in public places is another, and then there is the weather forecast ...

I hadn't realised on looking at the BBC weather map that Kent was as large as Scotland. And whatever happened to good old-fashioned isobars? Pretty graphics and moving raindrops may look nice but what is the wind actually doing? Here in the north-west, wind direction and wind speed is everything.

Take the clouds, for example. Our prevailing westerlies bring moist air across the Atlantic. It hits the first tall landmass such as the western headlands of Skye and is deflected upwards to condense as a regular band of cloud, sometimes pouring back from the highest point like smoke streaming from a chimney. Depending on the wind direction and which side of the hill you live, you will enjoy a sunny day and be hanging out the washing, or it will be thick mist and you set off with headlamps full-on only to have them pointed at by smiling faces when you reach the Post Office:

"It's thick mist just over the hill!" you try to explain.

And then the unexpected happens. High pressure switches the wind to the east. The whole of north-west Scotland is bathed in sunshine for days on end. (You know that it's bad everywhere else because the gloomy-faced weatherman starts out by saying: "I'm afraid it's going to be more of the same...")

East winds travel across the land. The air is deflected over prominent hills and crags and begins to ripple along in waves, causing clouds to form where air is rising and to disappear where it is falling. The resulting 'wave clouds' reflect the shape of the land they have travelled over.

During such stable periods we may see stacks of 'dinner plates' down-wind of the Cuillin, and 'fishes' and 'lentils' appearing above the Uists. Meteorologists refer to these as 'orographic clouds' meaning 'drawn by the mountains', or sometimes 'lenticular clouds' because of their shape.

Because the prevailing winds in Britain are westerlies, these effects are more often seen along the east coast, especially in the lee of hills in Fife and Aberdeenshire. That is quite a thought: could it be possible to say where a photograph was taken just by looking at the clouds!

For nearly 20 years I used to report the weather for the Met Office based at their auxiliary weather station in north Skye (actually the back of our croft), where I would creep outside at 0600hrs GMT in winter in my underpants, trying to read the thermometers inside a Stevenson's screen with a flashlamp; standing there with an anemometer held at arm's length attempting to record gusts in excess of 100mph.

Like other parts of the west coast, strong winds are a part of everyday life and have important consequences, particularly for crofters and fishermen, and for those who take their leisure outdoors. Like the Inuit of northern Canada, who have different names to describe different types of snow, we need words that describe different types of wind.

Residents of Foula, the rocky island west of Mainland Shetland, know all about strong winds. They experience a local whirlwind which originates on the western edge of the island and develops in the wake of Britain's second highest sea cliff – The Kame (376 metres). They call these winds 'flans', a word from the *Norn* language, which means 'to come rushing'. This seems the perfect word to describe a phenomenon so often experienced around our island coastline.

The airflow around a solid obstacle, such as an island hill or cliff, accelerates and shears away on the downwind side forming a 'separation bubble'. This is where the rotation often starts. Sailors crossing the lee side of Ailsa Craig in the Firth of Clyde may experience lines of corkscrew-shaped vortices sometimes turning clockwise, sometimes anticlockwise and sometimes alternating both ways. Against some sea cliffs and stacks, the wind rotates horizontally on the windward side and curls around the edges like a horseshoe whose ends trail behind in a rippling wake. You get a picture of this when you see snow drifting around a boulder, where the accelerating air cuts a deep channel around the sides. Multiply these effects a hundred-fold with a landmass like the Cuillin, and you can understand the forces involved and why Loch Sligachan gets such a battering.

But when does a wind become a flan? High speeds alone are not enough. The characteristic feature is when an eddy or vortex passes by in just a few seconds followed by a period of relative calm. Several flans may follow in quick succession – or there may be a long period of calm, which heralds the imminent arrival of a 'superflan'.

Many a time have I been kept awake, hearing the wind drop almost completely – the roof rafters cracking like knuckles as they move back into place – knowing that 'the big one' was on its way: the waterspout on the loch, the path of flattened rushes under the rising spray as it travels overland towards the house ... and then the sledge-hammer thud.

The pressure during this onslaught can change by as much as two to three millibars in a matter of seconds, so much so that your ears 'pop'. During such a storm, the pen trace on the barograph chart leaves a broad band half an inch wide, as the sensitive pistons and levers visibly jump up and down trying to follow the rapid changes in pressure. When *that* happens, you stay inside and just hope the roof stays on.

Orographic cloud forming stacks of 'dinner plates'
downwind of the Trotternish ridge in Skye

Climate Change

NEW SUNSPOT CYCLE WILL AFFECT LIFE ON EARTH

The influence of the sun on planet Earth, how it will effect climate and animal populations and the problems of interpreting correlations

One of the biggest events of the decade began in 2008. According to NASA (National Aeronautic and Space Administration) a sunspot was observed on the 4th of January, with a magnetic field pointing in the opposite direction to what had been observed for the past eleven years. It was announced as the official start of the next solar cycle.

"So what?" I hear you say. Who's bothered about some black dot on a disc that you can't see without burning your retina out? But it will affect us. From now on we are about to enter a period of increasing solar activity – more sunspots, more magnetic storms, and crucially, if the effect of past cycles is repeated, more global warming.

This is in addition to any increase in temperatures due to what is happening down here on Earth. We have been so focused on greenhouse gases, we have forgotten the other major cause of global warming – the sun.

Everything about the sun is big. The 'surface' temperature is over 5700 degrees Celsius. The core is 15 million degrees Celsius. The diameter is 1.4 million kilometres. The visible surface looks like an orange with a bumpy skin. Each bump is about 1000 kilometres wide.

And then it defies everything you ever thought you knew about matter. I remember in school chemistry being told of only 'three states': solids, liquids and gases. Well, you can forget all that. The sun exists as a plasma – a flowing mass of electrically-charged particles.

Every so often some of these particles are thrown out as a solar flare. We can't see this in white light but if you take just one colour from sunlight, a red wavelength called hydrogen alpha, you begin to see amazing things – explosions of intense radiation and charged particles shooting out from the surface, and 'prominences' that form columns tens of thousands of kilometres high before curling back along magnetic field lines.

And then there are Coronal Mass Ejections. It all looks so stable up there in the sky, but material is being continuously flung out into space. Typically once a day, but more often as the sun becomes more active, bits of the sun's outer layer burst outwards like an exploding bubble. Three or four days later, those bits aimed in our direction collide with the earth's magnetic field and produce an intense magnetic storm.

When you have an event that happens at regular intervals or in cycles, it's easy to link it to other events that are happening at the same time. This is the basis of (and the trouble with) 'correlation'. I remember I had a garden fork that broke about 20 years ago and then 10 years later, the replacement snapped. I'm convinced this is linked with the 11-year sunspot cycle.

It's quite logical: the increase in the sun's magnetic field that causes the increase in the number of sunspots also increases the solar wind which deflects the stream of cosmic rays and charged particles that would normally enter the Earth's lower atmosphere and seed the formation of clouds which would normally cool the Earth. More sunspots means hotter, sunnier weather which in turn means more gardening which means a greater chance of breaking the garden fork. Simple!

That's a rather concocted tongue-in-cheek example, but the underlying mechanism still holds. Consider the following based on more-carefully-gathered evidence. Between 1845 and 1935, the Hudson Bay Company kept meticulous records of animal skins brought to its trading posts. The numbers of trapped arctic hares and Canadian lynx peaked dramatically in 1854, 1865, 1876, 1886, 1895 ... every 10 to 11 years. It so happens that this correlates almost exactly with the peaks in the number of sunspots over the same period.

The hunting effort remained the same and yet in a bumper year, the number of hares caught was consistently above 60,000, whilst in poor years the number was always below 20,000. The statistics make a strong case for linking the breeding success of these animals with sunspot numbers. But does one thing cause the other or is this coincidental?

Despite such problems of interpretation, the link between the sun's activity and events here on Earth is difficult to ignore. If you look at historical records, the number of sunspots rises to a peak every 11 years. Our next peak is expected around 2012. The accompanying increase in magnetic activity will lead to more displays of aurorae, increased disruption of power supplies and further breakdowns in satellite communication.

For the past few years, there has been a sunspot minimum. In past centuries, this has correlated with periods of extreme cold weather in northern Europe – mini ice ages, major rivers freezing over, and snow at Christmas. All the evidence from direct observation and from proxy results derived from radioactive isotopes in tree rings, sediments and ice cores, indicate that up until the mid-1900s, the sun was the dominant force in regulating our climate. When the sun cooled down, so did we.

Even though greenhouse gases may be over-riding everything else just now, from the sun's perspective, the present solar minimum means this is as cool as it gets. Enjoy it while you can. This is our brief solar reprieve.

IN CELEBRATION OF CORAL

A walk along Dunvegan's coral beach. Examining the different types of coral and how they are affected by global warming

It was our wedding anniversary last month and I thought it time to do something special. In past years the entertainment has included looking for dead whales along the sea shore and examining land snails down a microscope. But this year it was 35 years and so it had to be special.

The man in the card shop said it was 'Coral'. And so it was obvious: a walk to the Coral Beaches in Loch Dunvegan. What better way to celebrate your 'Coral Wedding'? I might even find a decent piece to give to Janet for a present. Perfect!

But then the biologist in me said otherwise. You see, the 'coral' we find on our shores is not really coral but 'maerl'. It's a red alga. Pieces break off, get bleached by the sun and are washed ashore by the ton. It gives the sea that Bahamas blue and the shore that sweep of dazzling white. But it's still an alga for all that.

If we examine a distribution map around the coast of north-west Scotland, we find that maerl grows extensively all around the coast. Local divers will tell you they cross a sloping rocky threshold before entering a bright pink band of maerl scattered on the sea bed about 10 to 20 metres below mean-low-water.

There are three different types of maerl: one is found in completely marine conditions; the other two grow in sea lochs diluted by fresh water.

For the record, and to sound impressive, their names are *Phymatolithon calcareum* (marine conditions), and *Lithothamnion corallioides* and *L. glaciale* (variable salinity).

Extensive beds of maerl occur all around the Inner and Outer Hebrides and yet the so-called 'coral bays' are only found in a few places such as Loch Dunvegan and Ord. Why?

Many of these white bays share similar features. The Skye sites are west-facing and often have a small rocky island connected by a narrow spit of land that is covered at high water but accessible at low tide. Is this a coincidence or are these conditions necessary for the formation of coral beaches?

The key factor would seem to be the offshore currents. An offshore island such as Lampay in Loch Dunvegan or Oronsay in Loch Bracadale will intercept the tidal flow and the resulting eddies will lead to deposits of material in the region of slack, shallow water. The accumulating pieces of broken shell and dead coral will then be carried higher up the beach by the tide and the prevailing winds.

Above the shore and hidden below the grass are layers of white coral fragments. Some of them have been blown inshore by the wind. But there are also distinct layers found several inches below the surface. Some are graded fine sand and some are horizons filled with tumbled limpet shells and rounded pebbles. This marks the former sea-level – before the land rebounded upwards after being released from the weight of Ice Age ice. Geologists call these former shorelines 'raised beaches'. You can clearly see one, on the flat grassy platform above Dunvegan's Coral Bay: a 25-foot raised beach.

If you manage to visit a maerl bed at low tide, you will see that the living alga is coloured red. Seaweeds lower down the shore are often red. Red pigment is able to absorb light at those longer wavelengths that penetrate deep water. Seaweeds mid-way up the shore are usually brown. Brown pigment is able to absorb shorter wavelengths that penetrate shallower water. And then to complete the series, the seaweeds at the top of the shore are often green – to take advantage of the shorter wavelengths of direct sunlight.

If the coral beech is really a seaweed beach, then where can we find *true* coral? Most of us think of coral growing in warm water, forming reefs such as the Great Barrier Reef. But there are cold water corals that grow in British waters. These include the colonial soft corals such as 'dead man's fingers' and the solitary stony coral known as 'Devonshire cup coral'. But there is also a reef-building cold water coral (*Lophelia pertusa*) found in deep water, north-west of Cape Wrath on volcano-shaped mounds of sand known as the Darwin Banks. This same coral forms a 14-kilometre-long reef, 35 metres high – the Sula Ridge off the west coast of Norway.

Reef-building corals are related to sea anemones. They live in colonies of genetically identical individuals and form skeletons of chalk. Cold water corals live in deep water and feed by catching plankton. Warm water corals live in shallow water because they require sunlight. They take in a lodger – a coloured alga – that lives inside the coral skeleton. The alga pays its rent in nutrients produced by photosynthesis.

Whenever the sea becomes warmer than usual, the coral is put under stress and the algal partner is sent packing. The coral loses its colour, a process known as 'coral bleaching', and if the process isn't reversed quickly, the coral dies. If levels of carbon dioxide in the atmosphere increase, the sea becomes more acidic and the chalk skeleton dissolves or fails to develop. Either way, the coral dies.

Coral grows extremely slowly. Tourism, oil exploration and deep sea fishing, all pose a threat. But perhaps the greatest danger is from global warming. In 1997 and 1998, the sea temperature off Panama increased sufficiently to cause 'bleaching' of one particular coral species. All the colonies died within six years and the species is now thought to be extinct.

On a happier note, we celebrated our Coral Wedding with a great walk to Dunvegan's Coral Beach. True coral or not, it was the perfect way to mark a special day:

"Here's your present, dear."

"What is it?"

"A piece of seaweed!"

LAST YEAR'S WET SUMMER
RESPONSIBLE FOR CRUMBLY BREAD

*Examining the unexpected consequences of global warming
and its impact in the kitchen*

It's amazing how much science you can find in the kitchen. Janet was making bread the other day and commented on how it needed to be left baking for much longer than usual. And even then, when it was cut the next day for sandwiches, it was hopeless. The crust detached itself from the rest of the loaf. The bread knife gave up and became sticky and unusable after just one slice. The butter wouldn't spread but tore into the surface which then rolled itself into a gooey mass of crumbs. Disaster!

It's at times like this that you need to be careful what you say to the cook. I mean, she has been making bread for over 30 years now, and the last time she lost it was during the mid-eighties. Of course I said the right thing: "It's not your fault, dear. It's due to the large-scale oscillations in air pressure over the North Atlantic. Meteorologists call it the North Atlantic Oscillation or NAO for short."

"And how does that cause crumbly bread?" she replied, dragging yet another knife through the sticky loaf.

"The winter NAO affects the amount of rain that falls over Britain the following summer and so influences the quality of wheat harvested during that summer. High rainfall near harvest time causes wheat on the ear to sprout and produce enzymes that hydrolyse the starch. The resultant flour is rich in dextrins which makes the bread go sticky.

"Of course, this wouldn't have happened before we were married," I told her, jovially [long pause]. "Don't you want to know why?"

"OK. Why?" she replied, still holding the knife.

"Because we weren't a member of the European Economic Community in 1973 and that changed everything. Don't you want to know why?"

"OK. Why?"

"Because before then, we used flour milled from North American wheat. The EEC imposed import tariffs which meant that after 1973 we started using British wheat to make flour. British summers can be wet – as happened last year in the wheat-producing areas of the south-east – and that's why you will have difficulty making bread this year using the new batch of British flour!"

I always say the right thing.

I only mention this rather tortuous story to show how events that seem totally disconnected in time and space can affect us in the most unexpected ways. While we debate the causes of global warming, the effects are utterly unpredictable. Anyone who says otherwise has abandoned science for politics.

This spring I have been told of a number of unusual events. A resident of Flodigarry informed me of a hoopoe that appeared in his garden. What's a Mediterranean bird doing here in Skye? Last year we had an Australian black swan that stayed with us all summer after flying in from the other side of the world (Slimbridge, actually); and now there are reports from Skye of skuas coming down from the north, prospecting for new breeding territories; and of hooded crows becoming ever-more aggressive.

Successive mild winters? Who could have predicted the consequences?

And the changes keep coming: humming-bird hawk moths moving further north; mosquitoes and malaria spreading out from Africa; midges and bluetongue virus crossing the North Sea into Eastern England; New Zealand flatworm (*Arthurdendyus triangulatus*) hitchhiking all across the galaxy, just as its Latin name said it would.

Each Christmas we dig up a Christmas tree from the garden and bring it inside to decorate and then place our presents underneath. In 2008 we got more than we bargained for. The tree was covered in aphids. We didn't realise this until Christmas Day. The heat from the fire killed them all, after which they promptly fell to the floor. When we opened the presents, they were covered in dead flies.

Everyone, it seems, has a story to tell of how climate change is affecting things. But when it comes to predicting how serious it will be, we are still in the dark. The European governments are hoping to agree on a target of 450 parts per million of atmospheric carbon dioxide which they think will hold the rise in global warming to just two degrees Celsius. They argue that this will ensure minimal environmental effects. They don't know that.

If we run the clock back 50 million years, when carbon dioxide levels were falling, and the earth was getting colder – when the level fell to 425 parts per million, the Antarctic froze over. Some scientists believe we are likely to reach 425 parts per million in just 20 years' time. This could be one of these so-called tipping points, only in this scenario, the Antarctic completely melts and the sea level rises by 60 metres. But we really don't know.

As an alternative to this Hollywood-style disaster, some scientists believe that the melting ice will release the pressure on the earth's crust which will lower the melting point of magma and so lead to more volcanic eruptions – more smoke and dust and aerosols which would block out the sun, seed more clouds and cool everything down again. Some say the ocean currents will break down suddenly and the Gulf Stream will stop and Western Europe will freeze. We just don't know and the salutary fact is – our computer models aren't powerful enough to work it out. They can't even predict the high pressure patterns over the North Atlantic and consequently, when Janet's bread will fail.

"Well, Watson, what do you make of it?"

"Nice taste but a bit sticky."

"But who's responsible, Watson? Who is to blame for this heinous crime?"

"Well, contrary to traditional belief, Holmes, I should say the cook did it!"

"Aha! – Excellent, Watson! But unfortunately, it's not that simple. There is also the inconvenient problem of 'pre-harvest sprouting' to consider, not to mention the disruption of the Jet Stream, the North Atlantic Oscillation, the rising levels of carbon dioxide and methane, the changing solar cycle …"

STILL DREAMING OF A WHITE CHRISTMAS

The evidence for global warming. How greenhouse gases,
a varying sun and volcanic eruptions changed our image of Christmas

Snow at Christmas is an image we have grown up with. In the run-up to the festive season we see it on every advertisement. We hear it on every record. We've got to blame somebody and, as you know, I like to blame the weather presenters whenever possible.

When they say it's going to be a 'White Christmas', as though we're all going to be digging ourselves out of the house to reach the front gate and then sledging with the children all afternoon instead of listening to the Queen, what they really mean is that there will be a patch of snow on the top of The Weather Centre roof in Reading sometime on Christmas Day.

The 'problem' along Scotland's western seaboard is the Gulf Stream. It hardly ever snows, and when it does, it usually disappears overnight.

"Do you get snowed-in in winter?" asks a visitor.

"No, we get less snow in Dunvegan than you get in East Sussex."

But it's no use. It meets with complete disbelief. In desperation, I have found myself tramping over the moor to show them the pale butterwort, *Pingicula lusitanica*, and then labouring the botanical point that the name 'Lusitania' is the old Roman word for Portugal and Spain – which reflects the plant's affinity with a mild oceanic climate, and it's only found along the west coast, and you won't find it in East Sussex because it can't survive the winter frosts. But they still won't have it.

At the moment it's a picture of green fields and not much frost. In simpler times, before the increase in greenhouse gases, the main factor was the sunspots, or the lack of them. About every 200 years, the sun goes quiet and the sunspots all but disappear. In the past, when that happened, the Earth became colder, and it snowed.

Back in 1565, Pieter Bruegel the Elder was busy in his studio painting Christmas cards. There was always lots of snow outside … and hunting dogs, and peasants carrying bundles of firewood returning home to the women-folk who would be inside baking bread. And everyone wore black knitted bonnets ...

Alpine glaciers were on the increase. The canals in Venice froze over, as did the Thames in London. Historians call it the Little Ice Age. 'Little' is a relative term. It lasted between 1400 and 1800. It all took place during a period with little or no sunspots, what scientists called the Spörer minimum followed by the Maunder minimum.

And then in the early 1800s, just when the sun started becoming more active and things should have been warming up, several volcanoes started to erupt and the smoke and dust particles cooled the earth down once again. Most notable was the Tambora eruption in 1815 which led to the so-called 'year without a summer'. This was the period when Turner painted his red skies and Dickens conjured up those classic images of Christmas with lots of snow and ghosts everywhere.

By 1870, the volcanic dust had dissipated and the sun began to take control once more. But then by the 1950s, we started to see an increase in greenhouse gases. The graph depicting the steady rise in global temperature suddenly took an upturn – like the end of a hockey stick. Climatologists call it the 'hockey stick' graph.

That's the warning for the new millennium. More countries are becoming industrialised, and we continue to burn fossil fuels. There was a time when a journey to Portree was a big adventure (it still is for me), but now we don't think twice about jumping into a passenger jet and travelling anywhere in the world.

It all seems so simple. There is a cause and there is an effect – and yet the sceptic will point out that we can't be sure what causes the effect. Just because two events happen at the same time doesn't mean they are related or that one has caused the other. Scientists, especially social scientists, will frequently use the phrase: "Correlation does not imply causality." And so when you hear that the wages of Premiership footballers have risen sharply in the last 20 years in perfect step with sales of mince pies, it doesn't tell you much – except that somebody somewhere is eating too many mince pies.

We struggle to understand climate change, but there are so many factors. The Thames froze regularly and Frost Fairs were held during the early 1800s. This correlated with a period of minimum sunspots and the increase in volcanic activity. But after 1831, it never froze again. At first glance it looks as though the increase in sunspots during this later period was producing global warming. But some have pointed out that the old London Bridge was replaced in 1831. This led to a significant increase in the flow of the river. Some winters after 1831 were actually colder than before, but the Thames never froze again.

Even if we know all the factors, we don't know all their effects. Some regions will get warmer but others may get colder. In one scenario, global warming could have a cooling effect on Western Europe. If the mean global temperature rises by 2 to 3 degrees Celsius, some scientists believe that the ocean currents will be disrupted. The Greenland ice cap is rapidly melting and a river of ice called the Zacharia ice stream is flowing into the North Atlantic. If this flow increases, it could dilute the heavier saltwater and stop it sinking. If that happens, it won't be replaced by warmer water from the equator, and if that happens, as happened 12,000 years ago, then the Gulf Stream will suddenly stop.

All this is said in wistful mood as I sit here, gazing out on a warm sunny day – finishing-off a traditional Christmas dinner, followed by what is going to be my third mince pie.

Astronomical Observations Past and Present

IN THE WAKE OF A COMET

The wonder of the night sky, the joys and pitfalls of astrophotography,
and a brief encounter with Orion, hadrons and quarks

I remember as a young boy looking at one of the largest books I'd ever seen. It was called *The Splendour of the Heavens*, and it must have been all of six inches thick. It was full of magical images of the planets and stars – but what held my gaze the most were the comets.

There were woodcuts of the Great Comet of 1680 crossing the skyline of some medieval city. There was Halley's Comet as seen in 1066, caught on tapestry. There was a beautiful pen and ink sketch of Donati's Comet with a tail like a goose quill. And then there were the photographs: long time-exposures of more recent comets capturing the slant of stars cutting across the image like rain caught in a car's headlamp.

Spectacular comets are rare. You don't see many in a lifetime. Ikeya-Seki returns every 184 years and last appeared in September 1965, but I missed it – too busy listening to Beatles records. Comet West is even rarer, returning every 500,000 years. In February 1975, it entered our northern skies, but again, I missed it. Halley made its return in March 1986 – but I was too busy in the garden. This is hopeless. Didn't I realise I wasn't going to see any of these comets again?

So in 1997 when a comet was spotted with a spectacular tail, I realised this was a chance in a lifetime. This time I was ready. Its name was Hale-Bopp.

On a perfectly clear night, I waited, tripod ready, camera set with a three minute time exposure. The shutter clicked open. I went inside for a cup of tea and to keep warm. Shutter clicked shut. Got it! This was in the days before I switched to digital photography. I was using an old Olympus OM1 with 100 ASA colour film.

Out of the corner of my eye I could see the impressive curved tail being blown away from the sun. This was the debris of ice and dust that was breaking off from the comet's nucleus. But what I was hoping to see on the photographs was the straighter second tail, blue in colour, and made of ionised gas being pushed out in a thin straight line by the solar wind.

When the photographs came back from the laboratory, they were just the negatives, with a brief handwritten note explaining that as they were all *blank*, they would kindly credit me the printing cost 'next time'. After carefully checking them with a magnifying glass, I phoned back to say it was a comet – just a speck in the middle of a mass of darkness – easily missed by the lab and quite a relief for me as the 'next time' would be in AD 5400.

Nowadays, of course, there would be no such problem. I can go out with my digital camera, and snap away and check it immediately on the computer screen. And then afterwards in Photoshop, I could probably enhance this bit and sharpen that bit. And if there was nothing there – no problem – I could place a white blob in the night sky and then open a special dialogue box that would enable me to 'select comet tails': perhaps a choice of six different shapes including the classic Halley or a more flamboyant Donati; a choice of colours, widths, lengths and density ... Only joking!

Even if there are no comets visible at present, just standing outside on a clear night is worth while. Go outside just now and look south east. It's the Constellation of Orion that defines the winter sky, with the line of its belt pointing across to the brightest star in the sky – Sirius – also known as the 'dog star', because it occurs in the Constellation Canis Major. We see all this through our bleak mid-winter, but if we were in Egypt, these stars would signal summer, appearing sometime between 3rd July and 15th August. In ancient Egypt, the rising dog star heralded the start of the hot season – a period of intense heat and unhealthy conditions lasting 30 to 54 days – a period they called 'Dog Days'.

Orion is amazing. We call it 'the Hunter' because if you join up all the dots you get a broad-shouldered bloke with a belt slung with a sword. Tolkien's hobbits knew it as Menelvagor, 'the Swordsman'. If you look no further than this part of the sky, you will find no better way to terrify yourself. Here is the limit of our knowledge. Here is where it all begins. Star stuff.

I've recently been reading an Open University book called *How the Universe Works*. It's not really *reading* – more like turning pages and letting words go in and out of the brain. I mean, does anyone really understand all this stuff? Somewhere up there in the first millionth of a second after the

Big Bang, a group of up-quarks turned into down-quarks...

But that's nothing compared to what follows ...

It's the hadrons you really want to worry about, from the Greek word for 'hard bastards'. These things are flying about all over the place turning helium into carbon, and oxygen into silicon and then, after exploding inside a giant supernova, they set about creating all the rest of the elements that make up the planet and life on Earth.

And I thought evolution started in biology! It starts in physics. It's happening right now, up there in Orion's belt, all across the sky, in the birth and death of stars, beyond comprehension. Look again at that fuzzy patch of clouds and dust below the belt – what astronomers call the Orion Nebula. With binoculars on a clear night you can see it happening. The red patches are glowing filaments of ionised hydrogen: the light from a 'star factory', 1500 light years away.

As I tap away on this keyboard, the enormity of what I've just read has yet to sink in. If modern theories of cosmology and particle physics are correct, every atom of carbon that makes up every living thing, every atom of oxygen and nitrogen in the air we breathe, every element in the Earth's crust – iron, silicon and all the precious metals including gold, silver and platinum – all started-out as hydrogen, somewhere up there amongst the stars.

ON THE DARK SIDE OF THE MOON

The 'Goldilocks Enigma', the 'Anthropic Principle'
and the dangers of a posteriori reasoning

The depths of winter and the start of a New Year leads you naturally to thinking of times past. Thirty years ago I remember buying Pink Floyd's *Dark Side of the Moon*. It's still an amazing LP, especially when that female voice starts screaming at you, telling you to buy some *Ibuprofen* for the relief of headaches and such things.

I remember the day well. We had a Triumph Herald estate. It was hot and sunny and I carefully laid the vinyl LP in its black album sleeve – the one with the glass prism separating out the white light into a rainbow of colours – I carefully laid it on the back seat before driving home to play it on our music system.

The first track on side two is called 'Money': *Dum, dumty dum, dum – ti – dum ti dum dum dum-ti dum – Money*, and so on. I must have played it for years singing that syncopated rhythm to myself, along with all the other tracks. Brilliant!

But what recently made me sit up and think was the title of the album. Why the dark side of the moon? Why should it remain dark? Why can we not see the other side unless we travel in a space ship? After all, the moon orbits the Earth. You would think that occasionally it would show its back side.

It can only mean that it is turning just enough so that in one orbit of the Earth it has spun once on its axis. That sounds an incredible coincidence.

It all began over four billion years ago when a huge asteroid struck the Earth and ejected a plume of molten rock which solidified to form what we call the moon. Fortunately this object happens to have just the right gravitational pull to cause the tides and produce perfect conditions for shore life. It happens to be just the right size and distance away to produce a total eclipse of the sun, not too large as to block it all out, not too small to let the sun blind us when we watch, but just large enough for us to observe the sun's corona and to see sunlight breaking through the moon's mountains producing that sparkling display that astronomers call 'Baily's Beads'.

Coincidences can be seductive. Everything about our situation on planet Earth is perfect – just right for the evolution of intelligent life. Some astronomers with a philosophical bent refer to the 'Goldilocks Enigma' and the 'Anthropic Principle'. They believe conditions are so perfect and fine-tuned, it couldn't have happened by chance.

I have recently been reading a book called *Fooled by Randomness* by Nassim Nicholas Taleb. It makes the point that our brains are not suited to understanding chance events. We find it difficult to grasp the concept of probability. We are unhappy with events that are random, preferring to link them to an underlying cause: our own skill or some mysterious miracle or purpose.

The physicist, Richard Feynman, made fun of this tendency to give special meaning to chance events. He would say: "You never guess what happened last night. I went outside and saw a car with the number plate ARW 357. Imagine that! What were the chances of seeing that particular number on that particular night!"

The sun's diameter happens to be 400 times that of the moon but by chance happens to be 400 times further away and so when viewed from Earth we get a total solar eclipse. As hard-headed, no-nonsense scientists, we should say: "So what?", but somehow it's only natural (and part of being human) that we should stare in wonder and attribute it to some mysterious overall design or purpose.

But therein lies the danger. Once you start looking for purpose, you start reasoning backwards: X exists for the purpose of Y (philosophers call it *a posteriori* reasoning). Stephen Jay Gould makes the point by saying the reason the sausage has developed into its long thin shape is so we can fit it into a bread roll and make a hot dog.

All we can say is X exists and Y exists. And once we start looking for coincidences they can be whatever we want them to be. We are just the right distance from the sun to make Earth the right temperature for life to evolve: not too cold like on Mars, or too hot like on Venus, but 'just right'. The Earth is tilted twenty-three and a half degrees on its axis which results in us having different seasons. Its molten core produces just enough magnetic field to deflect all that deadly cosmic radiation. It has all the chemical ingredients necessary for life as we know it: carbon, hydrogen, oxygen, 1 lb white breadcrumbs, one and a half pound finely chopped or shredded suet, 1 lb Demerara sugar, 1 lb plain flour, 1 lb raisins, 4 oz chopped candied orange peel, 1 teaspoon ground nutmeg, 5 fl oz brandy, 8 eggs and half a pint of milk. Stir thoroughly and spoon into a well-greased basin and steam for 5 hours …and there it is – the perfect Christmas pudding.

As scientists, we can take life far too seriously!

Last year I heard Pink Floyd's album played on the radio. 'Money' started up. But it was different. No syncopated staccato rhythm. Just a continuous run-through of the lyrics. And I realised something was wrong – with my album that I bought those 30 years ago – the one I laid on the back seat of the Triumph Herald, in the sun, all afternoon, before driving home to play it on our music system.

Of course it had been affected by the sun. The black cover had absorbed the heat and somehow the tracks on that side had been deformed. It was amazing to think that I had listened to it for over 30 years – 30 years of playing it and singing it to myself without realising I had been listening to a deformed version. Until, that is, I recently heard the unheated version on the radio.

But d'you know the really amazing thing? … My version was better!

BRIGHT LIGHTS AWAY FROM THE CITY

*On first seeing the Northern Lights, and exploring
the physics behind their shape and colour*

As winter approaches, the one thing we have a lot of here in north-west Scotland is darkness – it goes with the territory. There's no point in being miserable about it, so why not enjoy it? Astronomers will tell you that the low population and lack of cities means that there is very little 'light pollution'. It's perfect for watching the heavens: stars, planets and things that go flash in the night.

A dark sky is something we take for granted, but in other parts of the world, it is becoming highly valued as it becomes more difficult to find. A recent study has shown that in the US, 62 per cent of the night sky is light-polluted. In Japan, the figure reaches 98.5 per cent, whilst in Germany, Austria, Belgium and the Netherlands, no part of the night sky is free of artificial light.

There was a time when astronomers built their telescopes on Blackford Hill in Edinburgh, but now they tell me it's no use – too much stray light: "We have to go to Hawaii where there's fewer street lamps." I could have suggested Barra. It's a lot nearer – but then I suppose there is more to it than that.

But there is one aspect where Barra scores over Hawaii. Latitude! What's so good about latitude? Well, the closer you get to the magnetic pole, the stronger the earth's magnetic force. The further north you are: the more likely you are to see the aurora borealis or Northern Lights.

Past Met Office figures suggest that some form of auroral display occurs in northern Scotland on 150 nights of the year. This compares with only ten nights in southern England. And so we are in the right place, and with the nights drawing in, now is the time to look to the northern horizon. If you see a glow developing, fix the camera on a tripod, open the aperture to maximum and get ready to take a 10 to 30-second time exposure.

An aurora may start as a faint glow, then develop into an arc, from which vertical rays may extend. Then multiple arcs in parallel suddenly appear, sometimes folded into bands and curtains. Rarely, on about ten nights in the year, the display develops 'coronal rays' which shoot across the sky, converging along the lines of magnetic force like spokes in a celestial umbrella.

For good displays you need the sky to be clear and dark, preferably with no moon. The best displays are often associated with sunspots which follow an 11-year cycle. At the moment, the sunspots are at their minimum, but if a coronal hole develops in the sun's atmosphere, charged particles can shoot out on the solar wind. If this is directed towards the Earth, then one to four days later, expect fireworks.

As the pulse of charged particles reaches the Earth's magnetic field it is guided along lines of magnetic force and slams into the oxygen and nitrogen in the atmosphere. This is where it gets exciting. Compass needles start to flicker. The night sky starts to glow. You are about to experience a full-blown magnetic storm.

The physics is similar to Blackpool's Illuminations, only there you have electricity causing neon gas to glow inside glass bulbs. Here you have electrons causing free oxygen and nitrogen to glow above our heads. Well, it's not quite above our heads: it starts at about 60 kilometres and extends to a height of 1000 kilometres. That beats the Blackpool Tower.

Turn off the house lights and go outside. Dress in something warm. Let your eyes get used to the dark (this will take about five minutes) and look up. The glow has now developed into curtains of white light constantly shimmering and shifting position. And then the colours begin. At 90 kilometres, oxygen atoms begin to glow green. Above 150 kilometres, the same oxygen atoms produce a band of red. And then suddenly at 1000 kilometres, nitrogen ions are turned on and join the display in a veil of purple.

If you are lucky, the whole sky will start to shoot coronal rays to a point called the magnetic zenith, which in Scotland is about 20 degrees south of a point directly above your head. I have only seen this twice in the past 30 years.

"Get up!" I remember telling our son. "Quickly, get out of bed and look outside!" It was two o'clock in the morning. He had to be up again at six-thirty to catch the school bus. He's never forgotten it ... never forgiven us...

There have been a number of outstanding displays in the past. One of these occurred on the night of 25th January, 1938 reaching a latitude as far south as Bermuda. In Britain, the event was characterised by brilliant red flares that were mistaken for huge fires. Later in the night, the vertical 'flames' turned green and yellow and developed into a full-blown coronal discharge covering the entire sky.

This must have been a spectacular event especially in northern Scotland in places where there was no cloud cover. I like to imagine the parents of some child in the dark wilds of the Hebrides that night in 1938, looking up in awe at what was happening above, rushing indoors to wake-up their young son or daughter: "Oh yes, I remember – they dragged me out of bed when I was fast-asleep to see some flashing lights in the sky ... never forgiven 'em!"

A CLOSER LOOK AT THE SUN AND MOON

Examining the scale of the solar system and the nature of the sun.
How moonwort got its alternative name

It's approaching the summer solstice and I'm being woken-up every morning by a blackbird singing outside our window. Janet keeps telling me to be more relaxed about it. At least it gives you an early start to the day, she says. But 2am ... I ask you?

Of course it could be worse. I was talking to a retired B&B landlady in Skye and she recalled how some American guests had complained at being kept awake all night by 'giant frogs', which turned out to be corncrakes!

It's our northern latitude that does it. I blame the sun. In mid-winter we all get depressed and turn pale. In mid-summer we all go manic and turn as red as lobsters. It comes with the latitude. Hardly any daylight one month: hardly any darkness the next. I swear that if it wasn't for the trees, there would only be two seasons.

Since Neolithic times, we have been fascinated by the sun. Stone circles have now given way to satellite telescopes. But we still find it difficult to comprehend what modern science has revealed. It's the sheer scale of the thing that is astonishing. It may look like a red orange the same size as the moon but when you read that it is '1.3 million times the volume of the Earth', well even that doesn't register.

I still have an old *Reader's Digest Great World Atlas*. On page seven it shows drawings of the planets and their moons alongside the sun, drawn to the same scale. I remember it inspired me to make a 'mobile'. It was a long time ago, when mobiles were things that were made out of paper shapes that swivelled on threads that you dangled from drinking straws suspended above a pram or a baby's cot. Nowadays when you say 'mobile' people think you mean one of those modern contraptions that are used to talk loudly into in railway carriages, where everyone in the compartment is forced to hear about little Jimmy's exam results or Uncle Bill's haemorrhoids ... I'd better stop.

To get back to the mobile that I made ... It was the solar system as shown in that old atlas. I carefully cut the shapes out of a cornflake packet. Mercury, Venus, Earth and Mars were easy – like a proof set of coins. When it came to Saturn and Jupiter, the cornflake packet was hardly big enough, but I still managed, and had them all suspended from the light fitting in the centre of the room. Then it came to cutting out the sun – the centrepiece. Impossible! Even if I'd had a piece of card big enough, the room wasn't! Dangle *this* above a kiddie's pram, and they'd have nightmares for the rest of their life!

What it brought home to me was the relative sizes of these things. Even the *Reader's Digest* didn't indicate the full size of the sun. We see the familiar shape and think of it as a solid ball when in fact it is a swirling mass of 'plasma'. It's like a thousand million nuclear power stations throwing out radiation of every type, most of which is invisible to our eyes. Only when you have a total solar eclipse, when the moon fits over the sun's disc, do you see the streamers, flares and prominences.

Brian May, the lead guitarist of the rock band *Queen*, took a PhD in astrophysics because of his fascination with the solar eclipse. The amazing coincidence is that the moon is at precisely the right distance from the Earth to completely cover the sun's disc. The moon appears exactly the same size as the sun! It's no surprise therefore that we have worshiped both in equal measure.

In 1765, the Lunar Circle was founded in Birmingham (later to become the Lunar Society). Its members included many of the leading thinkers and industrialists of the time including, Benjamin Franklin, Erasmus Darwin, James Watt and Josiah Wedgewood. Why was it called the Lunar Society? Because there were no effective street lights or carriage lamps. Members had to travel long distances over dark and dangerous roads. In order to make their journeys safer, they agreed to meet on nights near the full moon.

There is a plant called moonwort, *Botrychium lunaria*, which is one of the most diminutive ferns you are ever likely to see. It can be found in early summer on dry slopes and banks where sheep have grazed the grass low. Its paired fleshy leaves take the form of a crescent moon – a symbol often associated with magic. This probably led to it being used by alchemists to turn mercury into silver. I can tell you right now that that's a load of rubbish. It doesn't work. But what is interesting to a biologist is its alternative country name – 'unshoe-the-horse'.

You hardly ever spot this fern. Imagine then, being a soldier in the cavalry in the English Civil War. You are riding over a chalk downland where there is a patch of loose gravel. Your horse throws a shoe. This is where a horse would likely throw a shoe – on loose gravel. You dismount and look at the ground more closely than usual. There is this strange-looking plant like nothing you have seen before. This is where it grows – on loose gravel soils where the grass doesn't crowd it out. You see one plant and then you inevitably see another. That's the nature of spotting something this small hidden in the short grass.

This episode actually happened. During the Civil War, a whole troop of the Earl of Essex's cavalry suddenly lost their shoes on the downs near Tiverton – and moonwort got the blame.

Postscript

I have recently been informed that the poor moonwort has had yet another name change. It is no longer regarded by botanists as a true 'fern'. DNA analysis has shown that it is more accurately classified as a 'fern ally'. Such is life.

Maths and Physics in the Natural World

FIBONACCI, THE GOLDEN RATIO
AND NATURE BY NUMBERS

*The mathematics of rabbit breeding and why celery, leeks
and credit cards will never look the same again*

Fibonacci (ca.1180-1250) was the son of an Italian merchant. His real name was Leonardo da Pisa, a mathematical genius who travelled widely in Arabia. His nickname was 'blockhead' but he is remembered mostly for his sequence of numbers.

The numbers run as follows: 1, 2, 3, 5, 8, 13, 21, …To get the sequence, you add the previous two numbers to obtain the next one: one and two makes three; two and three makes five; three and five makes eight. In mathematics this is called a 'recursive' sequence.

The strange thing is that this sequence keeps popping up everywhere in nature. Take the number of petals in a flower: an iris has 3, a primrose 5; ragwort 13; marigold 21. And then there are daisies which have 34, sometimes 55 and sometimes 89 petals – all Fibonacci numbers.

It would appear that mathematics has something to say about the way things grow. Take rabbits, for example. Two rabbits breed to produce a new pair. On becoming fertile again, they produce yet another pair which then add to the original pair and go on to produce another new pair which add to the last pair, not forgetting the original pair … and before long you pass through the Fibonacci sequence with potentially 233 pairs (except that you don't because the fox takes 27, the otter removes 15, and the buzzard has something to say about it as well).

Bees also generate Fibonacci numbers. The number of ancestors produced after each generation follows the same sequence as the rabbits: 1, 2, 3, 5, 8, 13, …

The growth of snail shells can be looked at in a similar way by considering units of shell growth as an infinite sequence of boxes that spiral inwards.

The best examples, however, remain with plants, especially where growth forms a helical pattern. Some vegetables show this. Take cauliflowers. Look closely at the florets. They form two sets of rows: one spirals clockwise, the other anticlockwise. Count the number of rows and the numbers will always fall into the Fibonacci sequence. Whilst you are in the grocers, have a sneak look at a leek. When you rotate its stem 5 times you will have passed through 13 leaves. As for celery – better not mention the celery – I'm beginning to get some funny looks.

And then there's the stem of a hawthorn: twice around the stem and you pass through 5 thorns. Sedges: once around the stem and you pass 3 leaves. Pine cones: 8 rows spiral one way and 13 the other. The same numbers keep turning-up again and again.

The central disc of a marigold flower showing the Fibonacci sequence:
13 florets spiral clockwise and 8 spiral anti-clockwise

It all gets more mysterious when you look at the ratio between any pair of successive Fibonacci numbers. It approximates to the 'golden ratio' – 1: 1.61803... What's so special about that? Well, if you construct a rectangle using this ratio, you find that the smaller side is to the larger as the larger is to the sum of them both. The Greeks may have used the same ratio when designing the Parthenon.

We can see the same rectangles all around us: in postcards, credit cards, and photograph frames. It looks pleasing to the eye, which must mean that it looks pleasing to the brain. The big question is: do we find this ratio pleasing because of the way our brains are wired, or is it cultural – what the ancient Greeks found pleasing, we in the west accept as good form?

If you look at succulents including the cacti and examine the arrangement of the leaves or spines, you often find a sequence that goes 1, 3, 4, 7, 11, 18, 29,... These are known as 'Lucas numbers', a recursive sequence derived just like the Fibonacci sequence, by adding previous successive numbers. Successive Lucas numbers also lead us back to the golden ratio.

We can easily be seduced by the maths: the golden ratio is derived from a regular pentagon by dividing the diagonal of the pentagon by its side; the square of a particular number in the Fibonacci sequence is always one less or one more than the number derived by multiplying the numbers on either side of that particular number. Stop! No wonder I chose to study biology!

The common thread that runs through these numbers is one of utility. They provide the optimum way of arranging the growth of a plant to receive sunlight. It is the most efficient way of packing leaves and petals so that they have the most room. Plants that fail to grow in this way are at a disadvantage compared with those that follow this pattern. Here is the cold 'invisible hand' of evolution: random variation and natural selection result in the most efficient pattern for growth. That's the biological explanation.

In the past, Greek philosophers attached mysterious significance to certain mathematical forms such as the five Platonic solids. Fibonacci and the golden ratio have attained a similar status. But the plant meristems (growth points) that produce a spiral pattern just get on with it. They produce leaves, thorns or florets in the largest available gap between existing leaves, thorns and florets. It may give the appearance of mathematical design but the plant is not aware of that. It is our pattern-seeking brain that adds the maths to make sense of what it sees.

FLOATING ISLANDS AND INVERTED SHIPS IN THE MINCH

An old man and a young boy visit the sea shore
and discover the mystery and excitement of a mirage

"I can remember," said the man, "when I came down here, to this very spot on the shore ... and the boats far out in the Minch began to grow taller and the *Cal Mac* ferry looked like a block of white concrete flats gleaming in the sunlight. The islands appeared to be stretched above the water and the sharp edge of the coast, where the mountains went into the sea, became rounded and the land looked to be floating on air ... It was a mirage you see."

"What's a mirage?" asked the young boy.

"It's when you see a pool of water in the middle of the road on a hot day, but it's not really there."

"But I thought that only happened in the desert," said the boy.

"No, no – it can happen right here, over the sea ... Once, when it was getting dark, I remember a trawler that appeared in two halves with its middle missing. The front of the boat looked really tall, and then there was a gap with nothing, and then a block of cabins. Then an image of the two halves appeared upside-down and the light from the top mast was shining in the water below ... Scientists call it 'refraction' – it happens when the density of the air suddenly changes with temperature. Just now, for instance, with all this cold clear weather over the Minch, the sea is warmer than the air."

"But the sea is cold in winter," said the boy.

"Ah, but sometimes it's warmer than the air high above and then it causes the lower layer of air to warm up. When that happens, light passing through it will bend upwards, but our brains see it in a straight line. Scientists call it an 'inferior mirage'.

"Isn't it very good then?" asked the boy.

"No, – *inferior* means that things appear *below* where they should be. It's all a matter of physics you see."

"But I don't know anything about fizics," said the boy.

"Well it's not really physics," said the man, "– it's more like magic ... and it goes back to the time of King Arthur. He had a sister called Morgana le Fay. *Fae* is an Old French word that means she had magical powers like a 'fairy'. She was a sorceress and she used a special type of mirage to make objects appear *above* where they should be … When the Normans settled in southern Italy, they used to look out across to the island of Sicily and were frightened of being attacked from the sea …"

"Tell me more about the magic and King Arthur," said the boy.

"King Arthur's sister, Morgana le Fay, was believed to have magical powers and she could make boats float in the sky and then turn them upside-down."

"Could she really do that?" asked the boy.

"Of course she could – she could turn you upside-down if she wanted to, but she made it all happen above the water that separates Italy and Sicily, in the Straits of Messina – and the French settlers were amazed."

"And what did they do then?" asked the boy.

"They thought is was a magic spell and so they called it the *Fata Morgana.*"

"Why didn't they call it *Morgana le Fay* if they were French?"

"Because they were in Italy and they were speaking in Italian."

"Tell me more about the magic," said the boy.

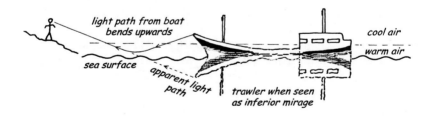

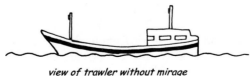

view of trawler without mirage

Ray diagram showing formation of inferior mirage

"It was a special Italian magic," said the man, " but it can happen right here off the coast of Skye – when it's cold in winter and the sea goes calm and it's about to get dark – then it's time to look out across the sea. You won't see it if you are standing too close to the water. You have to be at just the right height above the shore ... just here will do ... now stop talking and watch ... watch how the islands are beginning to float ..."

"And the boats – will *they* float too?"

"Of course ... Look! Here comes one now with a bright red band painted along its side."

"And will it turn upside-down?" asked the boy.

"It will. It will."

"And will the men drown?"

"No, don't worry. They won't drown," said the man. "It's all a matter of physics you see – it's just a trick of the light."

GHOSTLY SPECTRES IN THE BRACKEN

Especially for Halloween: an explanation of the 'heiligenschein' and the 'opposition effect' and where they can be seen

Halloween! It's that time of year for spooks and spectres. Sometimes I think they're all in the mind. But then when the sun is low and the shadows are long – beware! It's following you now, matching your every move ...

Raise your arm, and the spectre does the same. Take a photograph and it stands there, bold as brass. See it? The faint unearthly glow around its head? Its arms shoot out from its body like Edward Scissorhands. There's no point in running. It will match you stride for stride.

You're looking at a 'Shadow Spectre' sometimes called a 'glory' and sometimes the '*heiligenschein*'. What's that you say? – Some frightening foreign apparition that came across from medieval Europe? Created on the Brocken mountain in Germany? Formed around the heads of saints and painted by Giotto? A glowing sprite hiding in the morning dew? Is there no escape?

I stand in the late Autumn sunlight with a carpet of bracken below. It's a warm comforting brown with tints of umber and sienna. And then ... Oh no!

Shadow Spectre in bracken

Here it is again! It's no use thinking in this poetic language. Getting all romantic about it only makes it worse. I need an explanation or my imagination will take over...

Calm down. I know we've just had Halloween but I'm supposed to be a cold, calculating scientist. I just need to explain the thing in terms of a simple ray diagram. There's no supernatural ogre following me about. That's what I keep telling myself... It's just light doing strange things. Or, like Scrooge once said on meeting the ghost of Jacob Marley: "It could be a piece of undigested cheese or pickle."

But it isn't. I haven't eaten any pickle...It's the Shadow Spectre ... Ohhhh!

If you look out across the grass in the early morning when it's covered in dew, with the sun behind you, you will see the shadow of your head surrounded by a sparkling white glow. It's known as the *heiligenschein* ...and ... and, it's about to grab you and jump on you!...and ... sorry...sorry, I'd better get back to the science and that ray diagram ...

Heiligenschein means 'holy light'. It is one of several optical effects that are formed around shadows cast by the sun. But these aren't ordinary shadows. To produce these special optical effects, the shadow must be cast onto a surface that, when seen from the position of the observer, is exactly opposite the position of the sun – what scientists call the 'antisolar point'. This is usually formed below the horizon, but at sunrise and sunset, it may be seen just below your vantage point when standing on sloping ground.

The strange thing is that you only see the effect around your own shadow. If you are in a group and look at the shadows of other people, you won't see it. Each person sees their own *heiligenschein*. It is centred on *your* eyes only. The light rays entering your eyes have travelled through the spherical drops of dew to become focused on the blades of grass behind. They are then reflected back from the grass along the same path into your eye.

It's real. Take a photograph and it's still there. But now comes the spooky bit. Move the camera away from your head and take a photo at arm's length. The *heiligenschein* moves away from your head to encircle the camera!

When the drops of water are suspended in the air, as in fog or mist, a similar glow can surround your shadow. This is known as a 'glory'. It is often seen on a mountain ridge when your shadow is cast onto mist in the valley below. This time the light rays travel through the spherical water drops and are internally reflected back along the same path (similar to when a car's headlights are reflected in 'cats'eyes').

Like the *heiligenschein*, glories are formed around shadows at the antisolar point. What makes them different is their coloured rings – blue on the inside, then green, red and finally purple. Because the mist is three dimensional and ever-changing, the shadow at the centre of the glory will frequently extend back towards you, forming a grotesque shape with arms reaching out to meet you. This has been named the 'Brocken Spectre' because it is frequently seen on the Brocken – the highest point of the Harz Mountains in Germany.

But now comes the really strange bit. Shadow Spectres can form even when there are no water droplets. They have been seen in dry sand, in the canopy of forests, in corn fields and on hillsides covered in dry grass or bracken. The effect has even been photographed on the surface of the moon, as a bright glow surrounding an astronaut's shadow.

We can see this optical effect for ourselves, lighting up the moon's surface. It occurs at full moon, as it nears the antisolar point. Astronomers describe such a moon as being 'at opposition' to the sun. For this reason, the effect is called the 'opposition effect'. (A full moon appears brighter than expected if you calculate the increase in its brightness solely in terms of the increase in its illuminated area compared with the rest of its phases.)

For the opposition effect to work there has to be a textured surface full of its own tiny shadows. When you see such a surface lit by the sun at the antisolar point, the sunlight bounces back straight towards you. The result is a bright glow. But as your eye travels away from the antisolar point, you begin to see the textured surface as it really is, from the side, with all its side shadows.

So, for all you children out there – as 'trick or treat' passes into Bonfire Night – make sure you wait until the sun goes down. And whatever you do, stay away from dead bracken, for there lurks the Shadow Spectre!

IN SEARCH OF THE PERFECT HEXAGON

The mathematics behind one of nature's most-enduring patterns.
Explaining the symmetry in nature from basalt columns to bread rolls

Janet was baking some bread buns the other day. She asked me to turn up the oven when the buzzer rang and of course I forgot. The blobs of dough ran into each other and when the bread was finally baked, we had one giant bun.

I tried to tell her it was all worth while, for it proved a basic property of nature: where there are elastic surfaces, they move to their lowest energy level, and adopt three-way joints with 120 degree angles. I tried to explain all this but it was no use. She kept mumbling all day about how I'd ruined the bread.

Nature cannot do what it wants to do. It is constrained by maths and physics and in this case, surface tension. If the tension is even, it produces three-way corners with angles of 120 degrees. The exciting result in the kitchen that morning was that each separate blob of dough had pushed into its neighbour and formed a pattern of hexagons.

We see hexagons all around us: in packs of cotton wool buds (viewed end-on), corn on the cob, honeycomb, barnacles growing squashed together, soap bubbles, cracks in dried mud – wherever there is packing and cracking you will find hexagons.

Perhaps the most famous examples are geological – the Devil's Tower in Wyoming, the Devil's Post Pile in California, the Giant's Causeway in County Antrim and Fingal's Cave in Staffa. In north Skye we can find our own examples in certain types of basalt such as at Preshal Beg. There are also examples below Arthur's Seat in Edinburgh and in the Rock and Spindle on the south shore at St Andrews.

When molten lava cools slowly, the surface shrinks and cracks to form hexagonal columns. It's hard to imagine rock other than when it is solid. 'As solid as a rock,' we say – but molten rock is *elastic*. Its molecules are pulled this way and that by surface tension, like bubbles in a soap film.

When soap bubbles are held between parallel surfaces the tension causes them to pack together shoulder to shoulder with joints at 90 degrees to the confining surface. It's the same with lava. If enclosed between walls of rock, as in a dyke, the columns will be drawn out to form at 90 degrees to the confining surfaces. When this happens, you may find the rock has been sculptured into 'organ pipes' or stacks of 'pencils'. The columns may even curve to form giant 'ribs'.

Columns form parallel to the lines of compressional stress. It's a bit like the fine internal structure of bone that grows along curved lines in response to the stress from gravity and repetitive strain. I'm pretty sure I've developed some impressive stress-lines inside my right index finger in response to constantly clicking this computer mouse.

The cross-section of columns within rock is supposed to be six-sided, and this would happen in an ideal situation where the stresses are shared out evenly. But more often than not the cooling is rapid or variable and the lava contracts into cubes or pentagons.

The mathematics gets even more exciting, or bewildering, when you look at a curved surface. If you try and cover a sphere with a patchwork of hexagons, you end-up with a number of gaps. Take a close look at a football. It may look as if it's made-up of regular hexagons, but every so often, you find a smaller five-sided panel that has been sewn-in to complete the sphere. (Interestingly, however many six-sided panels have been built into a football, there will always be twelve and *only* twelve of these five-sided panels.)

Greenhouse domes like those seen at the Eden Project have the same problem – hidden amongst the regular array of hexagonal windows you will find the odd little pentagon filling the gaps. If the greenhouse is made into a complete sphere, like a football, it will contain exactly 12 pentagons.

When it comes to plant and animal life, odd numbers seem out of place somehow. Five sides don't seem as natural as six. Plant cells always seem to look better when drawn with six sides.

Take the liverwort *Conocephalum.* You can find it right now, lining the floor of wet caves and other damp hollows. It's the only liverwort I can identify with any confidence. [Who says I can't identify anything but lichen?] How do I know that it's *Conocephalum?* Because its surface is covered in what botanists call 'areolae' – separate sections – clearly visible to the naked eye and looking like rows of paving slabs: each slab with six sides, forming paths of tightly-packed hexagons; each hexagon with a large central pore which makes identification even easier. And if you're still in doubt – it stinks like a freshly-cleaned toilet when you squash it.

Symmetry is everything. Most animals that are on the move are symmetrical around two sides with a distinct front and a back. Biologists call it bilateral symmetry. Such animals have an even number of legs – two, four, six, eight, etc.

Starfish are different. In their young form (the larval form) they are bilateral – not that much different from a crab – but by the time they settle, they have chosen a life with five legs (pentamerous symmetry). Some have gone completely off the rails and chosen seven.

But I'm not having any of this imperfect five-sided nonsense. [Call me old-fashioned if you like, but I do like order.] Hexagons are what nature is all about. In a perfectly-regular flat mosaic, you never get pentagons. Crystals never have five sides. You never get a five-sided snowflake. They always have six sides.

And that reminds me of one of our Christmas decorations – a giant silver snowflake that we dangle each year above the front room window and it annoys me every time I see it, every year. *Eight* sides! It's more like a doily. I don't care if it is the season of good will. There's absolutely no excuse for such a shocking lack of scientific rigour in the design of festive decorations. No excuse!

Lichens and Fungi

SCOTLAND'S COLOURFUL LICHENS

A look at lichen and its links with Scottish social and natural history. Its role in the development of regional tartans and its use as an indicator of bird behaviour and environmental conditions

I bought some layers' pellets the other day and couldn't help a wry smile on reading the label: "Store in a cool dry place," it said.

"Where's that?" I asked, "Inverness?"

That's one of the problems of living out here in Skye – it rains a lot. But all is not doom and gloom for there are some things that positively thrive in this climate, such as moss and liverwort and lichen.

I like lichen: it's there all the year round, looks better when it's wet, people are impressed when you point it out, and are even more impressed when you give it a name. *"Lasallia pustulata!"* you say, looking down at the leafy growth on top of an isolated boulder. Perhaps it is the Latin that holds the spell. Unpronounceable names hide a secret knowledge.

There are approximately 1700 species of lichen in the UK and only a handful of these have common names. If a lichen does have a common name, then you can be sure it has been used for something, like a herbal treatment or for dyeing wool. 'Crottle' (or 'Crotal' in Gaelic) is one of them – turquoise-grey leaves covered in raised white veins, growing in wrinkled rosettes. (The Latin name, *Parmelia saxatilis,* refers to it being found mostly on rock.) If you look at a rock surface in this part of Scotland, the chances are it will have some crottle growing on it.

So what is this plant? Botanists regard it as a dual organism which means that two different plants have grown together to form a unique colony of mixed cells. The two plants that come together in this way are usually an alga and a fungus. The new plant has no roots. It grows very slowly, especially when dry, and can live for hundreds of years. Some of the oldest living things on the planet are lichens. In Swedish Lapland, there are some specimens that are estimated to be up to 9000 years old.

Here on Skye, you can find large white crusty lichens, like patches of tartare sauce, the size of dinner plates. Good examples can be found on the harder volcanic rocks where surface erosion is very slow. On average, these 'crustose' lichens increase their diameter by about a millimetre a year. If you find a colony with a 300 millimetre diameter, it must be at least 300 years old.

But what about the crottle? Unlike many lichens, it can tolerate air pollution and will grow on the outskirts of big cities. I have found it in the centre of Edinburgh on the top of Blackford Hill and Arthur's Seat. More typically it is found on acidic rock in areas of high rainfall such as here on the west coast.

People on Harris know all about crottle. It was traditionally used in the manufacture of Harris Tweed, to dye the wool a rich golden brown or yellow. If you own an old Harris Tweed jacket, you'll recognise the smell of the crottle as soon as you open the wardrobe.

The exciting thing about a lichen dye is that you don't have to prepare the wool in advance in any special way. No mordant is required – just boil the lichen with the wool, usually in an iron pot. Add some urine if you really have to.

The lichen acids react with the wool to produce the colour change, and the colours won't wash out. But such lichens were not popular with everyone. Fishermen would not go to sea with clothing dyed with rock lichens because they feared they would return back to the rocks.

Many of the clan tartans would have been developed using local plant dyes including lichens. The difference between west coast and east coast tartans is likely to reflect the different flora as you move across Scotland. The MacLeod of Lewis tartan, for example, has a high proportion of golden yellow, which probably reflects the amount of crottle that grows in the area. And the MacNeil tartan on Barra is mostly brown, yellow and purple – colours that can be derived from lichens found on the island's coastline.

Because lichen is closely attached to the surface, it is sensitive to the surface chemistry. Metals can have a dramatic effect on their growth. A lightning conductor on a church wall will have very few lichens growing alongside because of the toxic effect of copper. A similar effect can be seen on a roof and near windows where there is run-off below lead or zinc flashing.

This effect of metal poisoning shows up well on old fence stobs, especially after a period of wet weather. The next time you are travelling from Inverness to Skye, pull into a lay-by near one of the sheltered forest areas and take a look at the fence. The stobs will be covered in lichens except for the side where the rylock is attached. Here, below the top strand of wire, where zinc and iron is leaching into the wood, the surface will be almost completely bare of growth.

In contrast to this, certain chemicals will encourage growth. Nitrogen from bird droppings will lead to an increase in the mustard-yellow lichen called *Candelariella vitellina* (which roughly translated means: 'little yellow candle flame'). If you look at the corner post of your garden fence or a prominent boulder in an open area of grassland, the highest point is often covered in a yellow crust. This marks a regular look-out perch for the local birdlife. The Celtic crosses on Iona and the Standing Stones of Callanish – all have yellow tops. Fingal's Cave, Handa Island and Kilt Rock – all have ledges with the same tell-tale yellow.

Because lichens have no roots, they stop growing when dry. When their surface becomes wet, they make up for this dormant period, often swelling-up and changing colour. Some particularly healthy specimens have been found thriving on the walls of certain whisky distilleries – no doubt partaking of vapours escaping from the barrels!

So the next time you are out and about, keep a look out for lichen. And if it has a smile on its face, you'll know the reason why!

THE CHANGING FACE OF ANCIENT WOODLANDS

The impact of 18th-century blast furnaces on the
West Highland landscape.The ongoing 'coppice debate'
and the unique habitat of an Atlantic hazelwood

I have a fondness for south west Cumbria. I used to live there. Scattered throughout the area are numerous eighteenth-century forges that were fed with iron ore and limestone from the local hills. Charcoal from the local woods and water from the many rivers drove the blast furnaces.

In order to keep a forge burning non-stop for what could be a period of nine months, enormous quantities of charcoal were needed. It led to the introduction of long term woodland management in the form of coppicing. Oak, hazel and birch plantations were established and cut in rotation down to ground level every 15 to 20 years.

But the furnaces demanded so much charcoal that the Cumbrian woods were unable to supply the demand. At this point the forge owners looked to the west coast of Scotland.

Thomas Pennant on his tour of 1772 was the first to document how the forests of Mull and other islands were cleared to supply the furnaces of Cumbria. Later, it was found more profitable to build the forges where there was a sustainable supply of fuel. That's why the most complete example of a charcoal-fed blast furnace in Britain is situated near Taynuilt on the southern shore of Loch Etive. The birch and oak of Glen Nant supplied the charcoal for the Bonawe Furnace. The River Awe powered the bellows. The limestone came from Lismore and the iron ore came all the way from Cumbria by boat. Amazing!

But here comes the rub. In order to sustain operations, Bonawe required 10,000 acres of deciduous woodland coppice. That's equivalent to an area of 5000 football pitches. Vast areas of Argyllshire were drawn in. Even the oakwoods to the north of Loch Sunart were used to supply charcoal for the Glen Etive Forge.

Palaeontologists and ecologists will tell you that 5000 years after the Ice Age, much of the British countryside became covered in woodland . Pollen analysis shows birch giving way to hazel followed by oak. During this period of 'wildwood', it has been said that the woodland was sufficiently unbroken to allow a lichenologist to jump from tree to tree and travel from west coast to east coast without once touching the ground. [I may have got that wrong – it may have been a squirrel.]

The lack of old oak trees today is often put down to the fight against Napoleon. Many large trees were cut to build ships for the Navy. But the conflict also increased the amount of woodland that was planted for coppice and charcoal production. The Bonawe furnace produced cannonballs for Nelson's fleet. The demand was such that it kept the forge in business and the workforce showed its appreciation by erecting a commemorative plaque to Nelson after he was killed.

It is usually accepted that coppicing breaks the continuity of ancient woodland and reduces the variety of lichens and other epiphytes, but this does not seem to apply along the Atlantic coast of Scotland. Here, amongst the coppiced oak and birch we find branches and stems festooned with rare lichens and fungi. These are some of the best examples of temperate rainforest in Europe.

Lichens provide evidence of a long and continuous history of tree cover.

Thirty indicator species make up a scale called the 'Revised Index of Ecological Continuity' (RIEC). If any 20 species from this list are present, it indicates a wood going back to early medieval or possibly pre-Roman times. In certain parts of the Loch Sunart woods, up to 26 species from the RIEC list have been recorded.

Of equal international importance, are the Atlantic hazelwoods. Examples are found in Skye, Eigg, Mull and at Seil near Oban. These moss-covered woods are dripping with lichens. One hundred and eighteen different species have been recorded from hazel bark in a three-hectare wood on Eigg.

Many of these west coast hazelwoods look as though they have been coppiced. They have an ancient core or 'stool' around which sprout the new stems. But there is an ongoing debate as to whether or not they have been cut and managed like the hazelwoods found on the mainland further south. The continuous regeneration around a decaying centre could be natural due to storm damage or intermittent grazing or perhaps a less-severe pattern of selective cutting for timber and fuel rather than traditional coppicing where all the growth is taken back to ground level in one go.

Whatever their origins, these woods are a delight. This is where you find some rather special lichens which indicate the clean air and high rainfall along the west coast. Hazel bark is naturally more alkaline than oak or birch, and the tree canopy may intercept salt spray and so reduce the acidity of the bark even further.

Don't take these woods for granted. Some have been growing on these exposed coastal sites for up to 10,000 years. Forget the sunsets and the view across the sea. Forget Blaven. Everyone photographs that. Instead, point the camera inland, behind the line of parked cars, and focus on the hazelwood.

The young stems stand out like bleached bones against the dark interior. Take a closer look. The familiar brown hazel bark is covered in white lichen – known as 'script lichen' because it look like patches of paper covered in writing.

Go deeper into the wood. It's getting darker and more mossy. The lichens are becoming more leafy. Some have the dull metallic lustre of lead; some are bright apple-green. You spot a dead twig apparently held to the underside of a branch as if by magic – 'glue fungus'! If you are deeply into fungus, and all that that implies, you will by now be twitching, for once you find glue fungus there is a good chance you will also find the rarest of the rare – the 'hazel gloves fungus'. This peculiar beast looks like an orange hand grabbing hold of the stem. In Sweden it is called 'trollhand'. In Latin it is *Hypocreopsis rhododendri*, because it was first found on a rhododendron in North Carolina in 1888.

I really ought to get out more, and meet more people ...

FAINT HEART NE'ER WON FAIR FUNGUS

A fungal foray discovering the delights and terrors of 'food for free'

The recent wet weather hasn't been all bad. Thick mist with 100 per cent humidity is good news for fungi. They are currently springing up all over the place. Only last week, the top park seemed to be covered in horse mushrooms, some as large as side-plates.

I noticed a few brave holidaymakers (probably Italian), out early morning, heading back to their camper-van with a carrier-bag-full – no doubt looking forward to a delicious breakfast.

Most of us in Britain are suspicious of eating wild food. It isn't part of our culture to go out with baskets and bring back bits of decay and mould. In continental Europe they see things differently. Here, market stalls are often full of exotics such as 'ceps', 'chanterelles', 'morels' and 'truffles'.

We British restrict ourselves to the cultivated mushroom found in plastic trays under stretched polythene in supermarkets. The adventurous among us may think of collecting the field mushroom or the larger horse mushroom, but you have to be confident of what you are picking.

I remember some years ago collecting a horse mushroom – it must have been a foot across. I carefully brought it back and washed it. I cut off the base of the stem and sliced it. I carefully placed it in a pan with butter. Slow gas. Shook it like a pancake, turned it, noticed a yellow colour exuding out from the edge, consulted the textbook (again), served it on a plate, noticed the yellow, sprinkled it with salt and a little pepper – and then threw the lot in the bin. British you see!

But I really ought to change my outlook. After all, there is good food out there going to waste. And so I joined a fungal foray ...

It was going to be in woodland, most of which was Sitka spruce with the occasional hazel and sycamore. I was to discover that the type of fungi you find depends on the type of tree.

In front of us was a line of dark-brown 'toadstools', like an army of soldiers crossing the forest floor.

"*Collybia!*" said my guide. "Smell that! New-mown hay with a hint of cyanide – wonderful!"

[And I thought lichenologists had problems.]

The line in front of us was the edge of a fairy-ring that must have been at least 50 metres in diameter. It was moving out from its centre at a rate of nearly half a metre a year. Inside, it left a decayed wasteland: outside it was releasing nitrogen as it marched outwards across the forest floor.

A few steps further and we were down on our knees in front of one of the best known of the edible fungi – the chanterelle.

"Smell that! Apricots!"

Next was another delicacy – the hedgehog fungus, so-called because of the tiny spines where the gills should be.

"Taste that! Hazelnuts!"

And so it went on – fungus after fungus – each with a distinct taste or smell. As long as you don't suffer from sinusitis, identification was obviously a doddle.

'The miller'. Why is it called 'the miller'? It's obvious – because it smells of flour! This is easy.

But then – a sharp reminder – "Don't mistake it for *Clytocybe dealbata* which looks identical and contains the deadly toxin 'muscarin'."

"OK," I said, "I'll make a note of that."

Suitably scared, witless, I was offered a taste of the 'milk cap', *Lactarius*.

"Put a small amount of its 'milk' on the tip of your tongue. It tastes hot – like chilli. All the milk caps weep a milky fluid that's hot to the taste. The most-highly sought-after is *Lactarius deliciosus*."

"But will it kill me?" I whimper, crouched behind my camera lens.

"Of course not! You'll just pee orange for a week!"

Small price to pay for a delicious free meal.

The more I listened, the more I realised how much this mushroom-toadstool stuff was all about the olfactory and urino-genital systems. Take this for starters: *Phallus impudicus* – looks just like what its name boasts it looks like. Beatrix Potter refused to draw it.

Then there's the genus *Inocybe* – deadly poisonous (of course) with a characteristic smell that's described as 'spermatic' by those familiar with such matters. Beatrix Potter would probably have hidden behind the coal-scuttle for a week.

These fungi are not for the faint-hearted. And when I discovered that the poisonous fly agaric, *Amanita muscaria*, was used by Siberian tribes to induce a state of total inebriation that would make a Rose Street pub-crawl seem like a Sunday School outing, and that eating the fungus was only the first part and that the second part was drinking the urine that was produced after the first part – just to increase the effect. They don't do that in Rose Street. Do they?

This is no place for Victorian niceties. This is a down-to-earth subject linked with down-to-earth country names. Puffballs, for example, sounds reasonably inoffensive – well almost – but if you delve into the scientific name you find that *Lycoperdon* comes from the Greek for 'wolf fart'. [It's amazing what you can get away with if you say it in Greek.]

The main danger for the non-expert who likes to go out into the countryside and sample 'food-for-free' is mistaking the edible field mushroom for something that isn't. What's the problem? *Cortinarius anomalus* – the variable webcap – looks similar to the field mushroom but is found under birch and has rusty-red spores that highlight a cobwebby ring around the stem. If you get it wrong, like three holidaymakers did on a Scottish campsite in 1979, you'll probably need a kidney transplant.

Cooked breakfast, anyone?

CRACKING THE LICHEN CODE

Exploring the world of lichen and its use in forensic ecology

Watching wildlife, like any other venture in life, is what you make of it. Go down to the shore just now and you could easily come back thinking there is nothing there, except for a black Wellington boot; a small fluorescent light bulb (that amazingly is still intact) and a perfectly good toothbrush. It's too early for purple saxifrage, and so you turn away. But there are lots of things alive and thriving out there – even in February.

Winter is the perfect time to look for lichen and to try your hand at deciphering their names. The peat moor is a good place to start. And there's the first lichen, amongst the heather – *Cladonia uncialis. Cladonia* refers to it having branches; 'uncial' means 'inch-high' and reflects a form of writing found in ancient manuscripts using simple, rounded letters. Look closely. There's a letter 'Y' and an 'I' and a 'V' and possibly a 'J'. The branches and stems are all about one inch high: pale-green letters standing up amongst the moss and heather.

"Oh look! There's a message in the lichen."

"What's it say?"

"Get a life!"

Next is *Cladonia portentosa*: miniature trees used by model enthusiasts to create an idyllic rural landscape for a model railway – trees with many fine branches, like you see along the side of the station at Bridge of Orchy. And then there's *Cladonia arbuscula* (*arbor* is Latin for tree), with all its branches facing one way. It could have been swept by a south-westerly: the sort of lichen you could stick in plasticine between Strathcarron and Kyle of Lochalsh.

As you approach the sea, the colours on the rock change. You are crossing zones of lichen coloured grey, gold and black. The black looks like tar. When I first saw it, I thought it *was* tar. It scrapes off like tar. But under the x10 hand lens it shows itself to be lichen. It's called *Verrucaria maura*. It looks like a black verruca.

Stand on this black rock covered in lichen. (Incidentally, this is why some rocky outcrops are named 'Black Rock'.) Biologists call it the 'splash zone'. Another step towards the sea and you cross over onto a dirty-grey band of barnacles – the 'barnacle zone'. There is no more characteristic line around the coast than this. It is found all around the planet at the level of high tide. You see it on calendars of Portugal, and inside holiday brochures of Teneriffe and Hawaii. Don't you just get sick of seeing all those brochures as they drop out of the new *Radio Times*? Janet keeps leaving them about the place and last week she murmured something about Morocco...

But to return to Skye and the sea shore – and the barnacles. Just to show how exciting these things are, lay out flat just here. Take the hand lens. Now look closely at that barnacle. Do you see anything unusual about its surface? It's covered in tiny pits – tiny pin pricks. It's another lichen: *Pyrenocollema halodytes*, which roughly translated means 'a blob of snot sprinkled with pepper'. It dissolves tiny holes in the surface of barnacles. It is also found on limpets, mussels and limestone. Unbelievable!

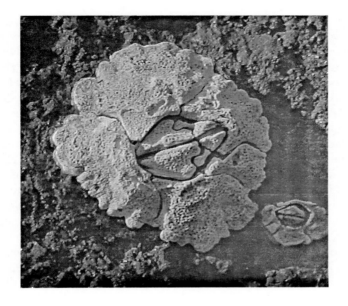

Acorn barnacle pitted with *Pyrenocollema halodytes*

This close contact with the surface gives lichens a forensic edge. I'm still waiting to see them in one of those *Crime Scene* TV programmes – telling us precisely where the crime was committed. There are lichens that only grow on limestone; lichens that prefer the acid bark of oak to the alkaline bark of elder; lichens that grow on silica-rich rock that is vertical and faces north; lichens that grow on horizontal well-lit limestone frequented by birds; lichens that grow on glass, on lead, on copper and iron … lichens that grow on the bonnet of an abandoned Ford Cortina?… Pure joy!

And then there is the way it grows, which tells you about the porosity and structure of the surface. There is a lichen called 'map lichen',

Rhizocarpon geographicum, that is so-named because it looks like a map of Europe: pale green and yellow countries drawn with dark borders with the main cities marked in black. If you find this lichen on the flat surface of a roof slate, the 'countries' will have a compact shape, like Austria or France. But colonies on the *edge* of a thick slab of slate will follow the grain of the rock and look more like Norway or Sweden. Lichens on granite form perfect circles, but on rock with a pronounced grain like shale, the lichens are drawn out to form ovals. The same occurs on wood. When it stops raining (it's better after rain), look at a fence post or wooden gate. The lichens follow the grain.

The good thing about lichen is that it can be seen all the year round, and in north-west Scotland, it is everywhere. You don't have to enter a camouflaged hide and wait patiently all day for it to appear. You don't have to climb 2000 feet up a rock face at a particular time of year to see it in flower. Just step outside and look up at your roof and it's there. The yellow patch on top of the gable-end is *Xanthoria parietina* (from the Greek: *xanthos* for yellow). It grows where there is nitrogen from bird droppings. It's on your roof exactly where it is because that's where that herring gull waits every morning when you go and feed the chickens.

If you wish to get serious about lichen, you can join the British Lichen Society. They organise courses where you can identify the more difficult species and get to know the significance of their names. Where else could you say *Pycnothelia papillaria*, or 'pimpled with firm nipples' in public? And what of *Umbilicaria hyperborea* – 'springing from the navel and found at the back of the north wind'?

And so we join our lichenologist and his companion – examining a shaded rock on which grows a dry powdery crust, coloured pink:

"What is it?"

"Another lichen."

"I don't want to be told its name ... I've had enough of Latin names."

"It's a good name."

"I don't want to hear it, OK?"

[long pause]

"*Belonia nidarosiensis* ... I thought you secretly wanted to know."

THE TRUMPET OF DEATH IS DELICIOUS WITH PASTA

An autumn foray to find the 'holy grail' of edible fungi

"Wear some old clothes. I've attached a rope to help us down the tricky bits. Bring the camera and a hand lens."

"What are we looking for?" I ask.

"*Trompette des Morts*".

"Isn't that the Trumpet of Death?"

"Wait 'til you see it. It's beautiful, especially with pasta."

Death by misadventure or death by pasta? What's the difference? You've got to go sometime.

First up was a Boletus (*Leccinum scabrum*), a sort of bun-shaped toadstool easily identified by pushing a finger into its top and then, after drawing your finger out, watching the impression remain behind.

"Can you eat it?" I ask foolishly.

"It's edible but not desirable."

Thank heavens for that!

We followed the rope down and entered a hazelwood: one of those places that the Outward Bound would delight in taking you and leaving you alone for 24 hours with just a piece of plastic sheet for a shelter, a sleeping bag, one raw sausage, an egg, some oats, a tea bag – and no toilet paper. Of course this was a gourmet's paradise if you knew what you were looking for. There were hazelnuts – a bit green, but still good to eat. There were edible fungi by the mouthful if you knew where to look.

"Try this! I think you tried it last time. It's a *Lactarius* or milkcap. Specific name: *pyrogalus*, which indicates a fiery taste. Try a drop ... Not too much or you'll be tasting chilli all week!"

Here we go again. I pretend to try it. I hate chilli.

"Now here's an interesting specimen – growing on hazel. *Stereum rugosum*. Also called bleeding stereum. You see what happens when I cut it with a knife?"

I watch with a strange sadistic delight as the skin-like surface of the fungus is slashed repeatedly with a pen knife, and then watch the weals of 'blood' slowly appear. This is more like it.

And then a warning: "Whatever you do don't eat any *Cortinarius* species. They are all poisonous. *Amanita* are poisonous too – all except this one,

Amanita vaginata, known as grisette. That's edible when it's fully cooked. The rest of the *Amanita* are killers." [What I would like to know is, who was the first to try the edible one to give it the all-clear?]

There then followed a stroll through what could have been an open air market with smells worthy of a St Andrews' chocolate shop. There was marzipan drifting from the upturned gills of *Russula laurocerasi*. (Where else?) There were jelly babies or *Leotia lubrica* – looking very tempting but I'll pass on those, thank you very much. No, not even my favourite black one, thank you.

And then we crept beneath the mossy branches to the spot that my guide knew well. He suddenly stopped and pointed at the ground: "This is it! *Craterellus cornucopioides*, the holy grail, or one of the holy grails of the fungal world."

I stare down at the trumpet-shaped growths. "Is this the Horn of Death?" I ask.

"The Horn of Plenty", my guide gently corrects me. "The French call it the *Trompette des Morts* because it is mostly black."

[Why do I keep thinking of that scene from *Indiana Jones and the Last Crusade*, where the villain chooses the wrong grail and his eyeballs drop out?]

"One of the holy grails you say? What's the other?"

"Chanterelles!" he says with a gleam in his eye. I'll show you some I found yesterday – growing alongside something that should interest you."

We retraced our steps and followed the rope back to the car. We were parked on a patch of waste ground that had been recently disturbed to bury some water pipes. Amongst the clay soil and sparse grass we saw what looked like small pieces of discarded orange-peel. This, I was told, was *Aleuria aurantia*, the orange peel fungus. It is apparently very rare in this part of Scotland. None has been recorded from the Outer Isles, and only a few sites are known in Skye and Mull. It is served-up in expensive London restaurants as a delicacy on salads.

Next stop was another hazelwood. It had all the signs of being an ancient woodland with growths of lungwort (*Lobaria pulmonaria*) and a particularly foul-smelling lichen called *Sticta fuliginosa*. Time to turn the tables I thought: "Smell that!" I said, encouraging my fungal friend to rub the *Sticta* between his fingers and hold it up to his nostrils. "Rotting fish!"

But he had the perfect riposte: "Smell that! ... Apricots!"

He had me beat. This was the second grail – *Cantharellus cibarius*. The beautiful smell of apricots wafted up from its deep yellow gills: "You pay a fortune for this in a London restaurant, and here it is for free!"

I was beginning to warm to this fungal foray business when he pointed out something growing a few feet away: "*Cortinarius*. Thought you might like to see it growing alongside the chanterelles. Don't pick it, or you could end up on kidney dialysis."

Are these things sent to try us? For every edible fungus there seems to be a poisonous look-alike. Earth balls have been mistaken for puff balls, yellow-stainers have been mistaken for horse mushrooms, *Cortinarius* have been mistaken for chanterelles.

I think I'll stick to lichens.

COUNTING TIME WITH THE SLOWEST CLOCK IN THE WORLD

How lichens can tell you when the dam was built and when the byre lost its roof

If you want to know when the byre lost its roof – measure the lichens on the inside walls. The process is called 'lichenometry' and it involves using some of the slowest-growing and longest-lived organisms on the planet.

There are three basic types of lichen: fast-growing 'beards', medium-growing 'leaves' and slow-growing 'crusts'. When you want to measure time, it's the slow-growing crusts that you need to look at.

Ideally, these lichens grow in circular colonies, like mould on the surface of jam. The older the surface: the larger the colony. If we already know the date of a surface – such as a gravestone – and measure the diameter of its largest colony, we can plot this on a graph, and if we have a range of surfaces with known dates we can plot a growth curve. The graph can then be used to date a surface of unknown age.

Although any slow-growing crustose lichen can be used, map lichen (*Rhizocarpon geographicum*) has often been the preferred choice. It can be identified as yellow-green colonies that look like countries drawn on a map with black lines marking the borders and black dots marking the 'cities'.

Most groups of cells grow to the rhythm of a waltz: 'slow-slow-quick-quick-slow'. Scientists lacking romance in their soul describe this as 'lag phase', 'log phase', 'stationary phase' and death. When plotted on a graph this produces a characteristic sigmoid or S-shape curve. But this is where map lichen scores. It produces a 'linear' growth curve (mainly due to its cells growing at a constant rate within separate regions)

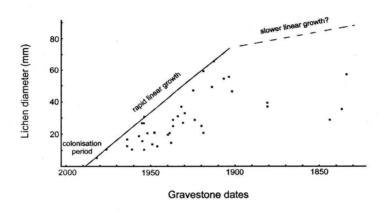

Growth curve of map lichen

Linear growth is ideal for lichenometry. (Life is complex enough!) The simple straight line represents a constant growth rate which in map lichen can last for up to 120 years. After this so-called 'great period', slower growth occurs which is more difficult to assess.

In Britain, growth rates are highest in areas with high rainfall. Map lichens near the west coast usually increase their diameter by about 1.0 millimetres per year whilst along Scotland's east coast, a slower growth of 0.1 millimetres per year is more typical.

So much for the theory, but how does it all work? First, identify the surface you want to date. Next, produce a growth curve from surfaces of known dates as close to the area you are investigating as possible. Next, find and measure the diameter of the largest colony on the surface to be dated and read off the age directly from the graph.

There are many limitations. We cannot say for certain that a surface is, for example, 50 years old – only that it is at least 50 years old. But that may be better than nothing.

The other point to note is that growth curves are often based on lichens found on the backs of gravestones, almost all of which are vertical and are either east or west-facing. When measuring colonies on surfaces to be dated, these should also be vertical and facing in the same orientation.

Lichens will grow at different rates on different types of rock depending on chemistry and texture. Growth rates are also affected by wind exposure, snow cover, pollution and competition from other vegetation.

Despite these problems, lichenometry continues to provide useful data. Map lichen was originally used in Greenland and the Alps to monitor the movement of ice. Wherever bedrock, boulders and moraines become exposed, lichens start to colonize the fresh surface. By marking the position of the same-sized lichens, an 'iso-line' can be drawn that monitors the path of a retreating glacier.

In Britain, lichens have been used to monitor the movement of loose rocks above roads prone to landslides. They have also been used to study the recent history of stone circles, revealing if and when surfaces have been cleaned or stones repositioned.

There is potential for some interesting field projects. I remember examining the rocks at the top of a waterfall and noticing a dry side-channel that had recently been colonized by lichens. The water level in the river had been changed after it had been dammed to construct a reservoir. The waterfall was halved in size and here was the evidence that linked the two events – the lichen diameters in the side channel matched those of lichens growing on the new roadside walls that had been constructed when the dam was built.

Tracing the history of old ruins that have lost their roofs can be a challenge. If you examine the remaining walls, the lichens on the inside are often smaller than those on the outside. Lichens require light and moisture and those on the inside walls will only have been growing since the roof collapsed. More significantly, their size indicates when the roof collapsed.

At a really practical level, the first hurdle in lichenometry is to identify the time-piece. Which lichens am I looking at? What is lichen anyway? If it were a bluebell or a primrose, there would be no problem. But there are over 1700 different species of lichens in the UK alone! Which do I choose?

Map lichens are not always present in this part of Scotland. In north Skye you are more likely to find rocks covered in grey patches with wart-like bumps and craters. Some of these lichens include the 'cudbear lichen' and 'crab's eye lichen', which were once used in the manufacture of natural dyes.

Any of these crustose lichens can be used for lichenometry. Their average growth rate can vary between two to three millimeters a year, and by using such rule-of-thumb figures it may be possible to obtain an approximate date for a surface that is less than a hundred years old. For longer time periods and for greater accuracy, a growth curve would need to be constructed.

A final word of warning: lichens can be addictive and may lead to obsessive-compulsive behaviour – even paranoia ...

[What you looking at me for?]

Alien Species

PESTS, POISONS AND BEAUTIFUL LADIES

How Belladonna got its name and how the humble earthworm is
causing us to rethink our attitude to pests and introduced species

Janet was picking some green leaves from the salad bed last week which
at this time of year invariably means last year's parsley.

"It's got more bitter as it's got older," she said.

"Tell me about it!" I barked back.

That's the trouble with going to seed. I'm referring to the Umbelliferae of
course – plants like parsley, carrots and celery that flower mostly in their
second year. Their leaf chemistry changes. And so if you want that fresh
parsley taste, you have to keep planting afresh each year.

The Umbelliferae are interesting. There are quite a number of wild forms,
some of which you wouldn't want to eat, however fresh they were. Take
the hemlock, *Conium maculatum*, used by the Greeks and Romans as a
means of execution; or better still, the slower-acting water hemlock *Circuta
virosa*, thought to have been taken by Socrates. The active ingredient is
'coniine', an alkaloid that paralyses the respiratory nerves. Death is by
suffocation.

One of the most well-known poisonous plants is the deadly nightshade.
Like the hemlock the poison acts on the nervous system, and causes death
by respiratory failure. One of the constituents is 'scopolamine' which causes
the pupils of the eye to dilate.

There is an interesting diversion here, involving physiology and human
behaviour. When we see someone or something attractive, our pupils will
automatically dilate. (Try this by looking at a photo of a glamorous nude
model and have someone observe your pupils.)

But that isn't the exciting bit. The exciting bit is that the effect is mutual
and we subconsciously recognise the effect in others. If someone find us
attractive it shows in *their* dilated pupils, and we find them attractive in
return. This is probably why candlelight is so romantic. Wide pupils make
for a beautiful lady. With this in mind it is interesting to note the Latin
name for deadly nightshade: 'Belladonna'!

Poisonous plants are usually left well alone because of their unpleasant taste or smell. Hemlock smells of mouse pee and most folk wouldn't touch it even if it were served in a straight glass. Foxgloves are extremely bitter. That's why these plants are left alone and are so widespread. Even members of the buttercup family, like the lesser celandine contain a poison, 'proto-anemonin', a yellow oil that causes inflammation of the mouth and stomach. When you see a field full of yellow flowers, you know the animals have been selective in what they've eaten.

Bracken is another plant that is avoided by grazing animals. It has a concoction of poisons. As the plant develops through the summer, it produces cyanide. The leaves also contain enzymes that remove vitamin B. This isn't a problem in animals with a second stomach where bacteria produce vitamins, but in non-ruminants, such as horses and pigs, bracken can cause vitamin B deficiency.

In the garden it has been a time for digging. After many years of adding organic matter, the worms are a good sign. It is with some dismay, therefore, to hear that our common earthworm, *Lumbricus terrestris*, is now under threat from an overseas predator. The New Zealand flatworm, *Arthurdendyus triangulatus*, is gaining ground fast. It kills our native worm by injecting it with a paralysing enzyme and then proceeds to eat it alive. Gardeners are being warned to be on the lookout for this new invader.

This highlights a problem of attitude towards pests and introduced species. What we regard as friend or foe depends on where we live. In the US and Canada, there shouldn't be any earthworms north of a line that runs west from Boston. The leaf litter in these northern woodlands is much thicker than is found in European forests, and has an average depth of 10 to 15 centimetres. This loose layer supports an exceptionally-rich variety of plant and animal species and relies on beetles, salamanders and small mammals for aeration. But all this is changing. The delicate ecosystem of the deep leaf litter is being destroyed by an imported pest. What could be causing the damage?

Biologists have found six alien worms chewing up the forest floor. The chief culprits are from Britain – non other than our friendly European earthworm, *L. terrestris*. And what answer is being considered by some biologists? To introduce the New Zealand flatworm! Crazy world!

It may come as a shock to hear that our humble earthworm is not universally welcomed. What we regard as a valuable aid to soil improvement, producing burrows to aerate and drain the soil, and worm casts that are home to friendly nitrifying bacteria – over in North America, all this spells death to wild flowers. One reason is the large numbers of deer that roam the woodlands and trample the ground. The reduced depth of leaf litter means that the soil becomes hard-packed and plant seedlings cannot take root.

If you have a lawn, matters can get serious. Worm casts spoil the look of that perfect surface. You used to be able to get a liquid that was watered into the grass and caused the worms to rise to the surface. I remember as a young boy being sent out to gather up worms from our lawn that had been treated in this way. I collected nearly a bucketful.

I've just finished watching the golf on telly – The Masters, held in Augusta, Georgia. Perfect fairways. Perfect greens. Perfect weather. Doesn't it make you sick! Not a breath of wind. Not even a ripple in the water below that bloomin' bridge – and even that, I'm told, has a fitted carpet, coloured green of course.

Anyway – they could be in for trouble quite soon. The Asian worm, *Amyanthus*, has moved in. It was probably introduced as fishing bait, for which it is particularly good. Unlike the European invaders, this species is big. It can grow to the size of a pencil and it's going to play havoc with those greens. Come the next Masters, I might just go and enquire if they need any help. I'm still pretty good with a bucket.

'ALIENS' SPOTTED IN DUNVEGAN GARDEN

Our attitude to invasive species
with particular reference to Japanese knotweed

Janet was reading a garden catalogue that came through the post:
   "Do you want the good news first?"
   "What?"
   "Buy twenty – get ten free!"
   "And the bad news?
   "They're creeping buttercups!"

It's true – they were actually selling creeping buttercups. Presumably they've done their research and somebody somewhere is buying them. Maybe I should stop being so cynical. Maybe there's a way to make some money here – a sign on the roadside: "Pick your own buttercups. Dig as many as you want. Fifty for a pound. Fork supplied."

But it does make you think about our attitudes towards plants. It's now the ecologically-done-thing to grow what only a few decades ago were regarded as weeds. You can buy packets of wildflower seeds – and do your bit for nature and the environment. But beware! Some packets of 'Scottish Wildflower Seeds' on sale locally don't contain any seeds native to Scotland. Some of them contain seeds that aren't even native to the British Isles.

Plants go in and out of fashion. Take the daisy family. I've got plenty in the lawn. I'm constantly being told by garden experts to get rid of them and then in the next breath they recommend a new coloured variety to fill the border – *Bellis pinkyredii*, or some such name. It's a daisy I say! It may have a slightly bigger head and a different tinge of colour, but it's still a daisy. So I carefully dig out all those nasty white flowers and buy some of those expensive pink ones? Maybe its time to rethink our attitude to 'weeds'.

A weed has been called 'a plant in the wrong place'. That may hold for the garden, but in the wild it's not that simple. The distinction between what is natural and what is 'alien' or introduced is now completely blurred. I was on a guided walk in a hazelwood earlier this year. Suddenly someone shouted: "*Osmunda regalis!*" We all turned round to see this one patch of 'royal fern'. But was it natural or had it been planted there?

It's a nightmare for botanists who are compiling a flora of a particular area. Take a walk in parts of Suardal, for instance, and you will likely find more cotoneaster than birch or ash. There's a well-known patch of fuschia growing alongside the Scorrybreac path outside Portree – and what of that single fritillary flower in the middle of a grass field near Plockton?

Victorians were fond of introducing different plants – the new and the exotic from all around the world. Take a walk in the vicinity of any 'big-house' garden and you will find plants from Canada and New Zealand that have escaped over the garden walls. One of the worst invaders comes from Spain and the Caucases – the common rhododendron, *Rhododendron ponticum*. Large areas of the West Highlands provide it with the perfect habitat where it out-competes the native oak and birch.

Geoff Collins, former Head Gardener at Inverewe, tells me that

Rhododendron ponticum can be a problem in sheltered woodland where it spreads quickly by horizontal 'layering'. He was offered the services of a working party of teenage boys to clear excess growth from the Inverewe grounds. The process was affectionately known as 'ponti-bashing'. The lads were provided with axes and saws and set to work with great enthusiasm. There was one problem: half the group came from Borstal – part of a social worker's programme of confidence building ... Geoff tells it with characteristic understatement: "There was plenty of 'confidence building' going on – but 'plant identification' was not one of their strong points!"

We could blame this legacy on the Victorians. As well as the rhododendrons, they introduced trees such as beech and sycamore from more southern parts of Britain. The wrong trees for this part of the country? Trees that grow too fast? We should be so lucky! In our garden, I'm glad if any tree survives, given the winds we get in this part of Skye.

But there are some introduced plants that grow too well and have become a national problem. One of them has been singled out for special mention – Japanese knotweed, now regarded as Britain's most-invasive plant. I have been told that it is becoming a real threat in the Dunvegan area and residents are being asked to be on the lookout. If you find it in your garden you're advised to try and get rid of it.

But it won't be easy – it's like trying to get rid of horseradish, only worse. You could try digging it out. I recommend a JCB with a specially-reinforced bucket ... I shouldn't joke. It is a serious matter. Once established, the roots can reach a depth of ten feet or more. It can grow through concrete at speeds of up to two centimetres a day. That's serious.

One generation's ornament is another generation's problem. It isn't a problem yet in Scotland, but down in England at the moment, they are fighting a battle against another introduced species – the Himalayan balsam. (Why are all these plants from the Himalayas?) Like the knotweed, this was introduced by the Victorians in the mid-1800s. It is taking-over riverbanks and excluding most other plants because there are no natural predators to keep it in check.

WHEN FURRY FRIENDS BECOME FURRY FOES

The story of how moles were introduced to Skye
highlights our cultural attitudes to different animals

If you want to spot a stoat, watch the birds. Take a closer look at that old stone dyke. Suddenly, a wheatear begins its alarm call – "wheet-chack-chack, wheet-chack-chack!" Seconds later, a stoat appears on cue.

I remember one such encounter. The stoat emerged from a rabbit hole dragging a rabbit that must have been at least twice its size. It crossed a grass slope for 20 metres before disappearing down another hole.

Later that day, I took Janet to the same spot. I had attached the telephoto lens to the camera. If anything emerged this time, I was going to catch it in close-up.

We settled down behind a turf bank. I focused the camera on the hole where the stoat had disappeared: "Keep an eye on that rabbit hole," I said.

I took the car keys from my pocket and jangled them in my hand. It was worth a try. You see, I had read that the sound of car keys being jangled can attract a stoat. It was nonsense of course – I mean, why should a stoat be interested in anyone's car keys?

And then to our amazement – a stoat poked its head out of the hole!

["What? – Just a Suzuki *Alto*?"]

Stoats are one of the few animals that don't run away when they see you. They are inquisitive, like grey seals that swim towards you and watch what you are doing on the shore. This one was mesmerised by the tripod and camera equipment. Out it came, then another … and another … and another …and another. The whole family came out. Quick get a photo. Bloomin' heck! They were all around us, doing somersaults and chasing each other in circles. Can't follow them. The camera's on a tripod because of the telephoto … But it makes no difference – they're too close for the lens!

We came away with an indelible memory but with just a blurred image on film, of stoats in mid-air chasing their tails.

Our attitudes to such things depend on personal circumstances. Anything with large eyes and a furry face makes us go all gooey and sentimental. Unless, that is, you keep chickens. Stoats, like foxes and ferrets, do not mix well with chickens.

We have a vegetable garden. I like frogs because they eat slugs. I don't want to see rabbits. But if you aren't growing lettuce and carrots, the chances are you will hold the exact opposite view.

Attitudes are also fixed by tradition and culture. Rats are often despised as vermin in the West, but in the East, they are admired for their quick wits and self-reliance. A recent Chinese New Year was named 'The Year of the Rat'. It didn't mean that bad times were just ahead, with a return of the plague – and 'babies bitten in the cradles', and 'soup licked from the cooks' own ladles'. In China and Japan there are no such fears, and the rat continues to be a symbol of good luck and wealth.

Perhaps the rat's continuing bad press in the West comes from a tendency of rodents in northern Europe and the Arctic to appear in 'plagues'. Lemming numbers are often seen to peak every four years. The number of rats and mice can also fluctuate dramatically from year to year. It has been suggested that mouse plagues throughout Germany in 1917 and 1918 contributed to Germany's defeat in the Great War. The effects on agriculture and food production were critical when coupled with the impact of the British naval blockade.

In parts of Skye this winter we have had what could be described as a plague of field voles. I usually leave our main-crop carrots in the ground to be dug-up when needed, but this year, they were completely eaten away.

Children's books have a great influence on attitudes. Take moles. Who wouldn't be moved by that scene in the snow when Mole in *The Wind in the Willows* is cajoled by his friend, Ratty, to keep moving, even though he could smell his old home and was desperate to stop and find it? We are left with an enduring image of a gentle furry creature with eyes closed and a sense of helplessness.

And then one day they enter your garden. Moles need to eat their weight in worms every day. You spend all year preparing the compost heap and in one night, the worms have gone! Paths are undermined. Fence posts keel over.

Lord Napier of Magdala was the man responsible for bringing them to Skye. He lived at Lyndale House where it is documented in the Estate Accounts: purchase of moles; 20th July 1903 – '£2-2s-0d'. They were sent by post in a canvas bag and arrived at the Edinbane Post Office where they escaped briefly – causing considerable upset as they were mistaken for rats – before being recaptured. They were destined for the Ascrib Islands to help improve the soil for the sheep-grazing. But the weather conspired against the transfer and so they were released in the grounds of Lyndale House.

What happened next is given in the Accounts Book eight years later: July 4th 1911, 'paid for mole traps from CGA (Country Gentleman's Association) – £1-4s-0d.'

And then on the next line: 'mole trapping – £2-0s-0d.'

Two lines that speak volumes.

The story has even been put into verse and made into a song: 'The Moles' available on a CD (*Edinbanter*, a Community Identity Project).

Today, they are spreading out from their Lyndale epicentre. So far they have reached Lovaig Bay above Dunvegan in the west, the head of Loch Snizort in the east, Ullinish to the south and Hallin in Waternish to the north. Glendale is still a mole-free zone but if they continue tunnelling at the same rate they will be here by 2108.

Time yet before we hear that fearful cry: "Lock up your worms – the moles are coming!"

The Effects of Competition

LIVING WITH SALT: THE SCURVY-GRASS MYSTERY

How plants and animals adapt to salt,
its impact along the exposed west coast of Scotland
and some unexpected effects inland

Strange stuff salt. Put it on herring and it preserves it. Put it on your car and it rots it away.

We had a gale the other day and to make matters worse – the sun came out. Janet now tells me we need the windows cleaning again.

"It's not dirt, it's salt," I tell her.

"But they are all white and we can't see out."

I remember for two years running – in April, just when the spring growth had begun – I remember driving through Kintail and seeing all the birch burnt down their west-facing sides. You could have drawn a line down the middle of each tree; each looked like two different plants. When I got home, I noticed the roses had turned black overnight. There had been a prolonged westerly gale, but it wasn't the wind that had turned the leaves black. It was salt.

That's one of the problems of living near the sea – whether you are a gardener or are trying to stop the car from rusting or need to keep the windows clean. When the wind blows, there is always salt in the air.

Gardening in exposed sites is not just about the physical effects of the wind. There is the added factor of rapid dehydration caused by sea salt. I planted some hybrid willows to make a windbreak. After three or four years of rapid growth they all began to die. The bark was too soft and the combined effects of wind and salt began to take their toll. Now I prune them back to encourage new growth. This has to be done each year but at least they now stay alive.

Take a walk down to the shore in December, any shore will do, and look at the leaves that are still surviving. The main problem for living tissue near the sea is dehydration (salt removes water by osmosis). Plants have developed a number of strategies to counter this. Look at the lush growth of leaves cascading down from the cliff. Sailors from long ago named it 'scurvy-grass'. It's a member of the cabbage family and it's rich in vitamin C. It survives here, splashed by salt spray, because the leaves are shiny – covered in wax. The same strategy is used by some varieties of *Olearia* or New Zealand holly, which does so well in exposed gardens.

If you can't cover yourself in wax, make yourself hairy. The downy birch, *Betula pubescens*, has twigs and buds covered in downy hair, and is able to withstand dehydration better than the silver birch, *Betula pendula*. There is also the downy currant, *Ribes spicatum*, which grows in various exposed boulder fields around the coast. Its leaves are covered in fine hairs to hold the salt-laden moisture at bay. The fruit has a tang of chloroform – a bit like Victory-V lozenges.

If wax and hair aren't available, then reduce your surface area. Almost all the plants that hold onto their leaves in winter have worked this out: squat stubby leaves, like heather; needle-shaped leaves, like 'prostrate' juniper [why do I always say this name wrong? – must be my age]; leaves that fold in half to reduce evaporation, like matt grass; leaves that roll into a tube, like crowberry.

Crowberry *(Empetrum nigrum)* is a good example. On your way back from the shore, look closely at what can easily be mistaken for heather. Even now, in December, the occasional plant still has its characteristic black berries. Most have been eaten by crows and other birds, although I did find a patch full of berries, dangling down from an overhanging quarry edge, significantly where no bird could land.

How can you tell it is crowberry if it has lost all its berries? Look closely at the leaf. There is a thin white line running along the back like a thin seam. And that's exactly what it is. It's a seam where the leaf has rolled into a tube and the edges have part-fused together. This mathematical device stops the plant from losing excess water – the outside of a tube has less surface area than both sides of a flat sheet.

We were visiting friends in Perthshire last month and happened to spot a waxy plant growing along the side of the A9. On closer examination it turned out to be Danish scurvy-grass. Sherlock Holmes would have enjoyed this:

"Alright, Watson – what do you make of it?

"What am I looking at, Holmes?"

"Danish scurvy-grass, *Cochlearia danica* – highly unusual and until recently, only found along the coast. And yet here it is – growing as far away from the sea as possible – in the centre of Scotland."

"Perhaps it was planted deliberately or it escaped from a nearby garden?"

"No, Watson – there is something much more subtle at work here."

"You have the better of me, Holmes."

"Well, consider what is used to keep this road open in winter."

"Gravel and sand?"

"Exactly, my friend – but what is more relevant here is that gravel and sand are sometimes brought in from the coast."

"But why is the plant growing so well along the edge of this main trunk road?"

"Salt, Watson! The gritting lorries use salt!"

Animals can also thrive in habitats where there are high levels of salt. Seabirds have mastered the marine environment, helped by their ability to drink seawater. Sometimes it is their only source of drinking water, and they have a special way of getting rid of the salt. All birds have 'salt glands' located next to the eye. In seabirds these are particularly active, producing a concentrated salt solution which drains through small holes or slits on top of the beak.

Sharks also have salt glands. Bony fish get rid of excess salt through their gills. Crocodiles drip salt from their nasal glands (possibly the origin of 'crocodile tears'). As for *Homo sapiens*, we seem to have conquered every corner of the globe with just a pair of kidneys.

COMPETITION FORCES PLANTS
TO GROW IN THE STRANGEST PLACES

The distribution of plants underneath washing lines,
lead spoil heaps and electricity pylons

It's a competitive world out there – and yet help may come from the most unexpected quarters. Take our washing line, for example. Who would have thought it had such an important role to play in affecting plant survival?

Look closely at the grass, underneath the line, marked-out as if with a ruler: a white band of clover, half a metre wide. The flowers grow parallel with the washing line but not exactly below the line. They grow slightly upwind of the line by about an arm's length. There's the puzzle, and there's the clue.

Whenever someone hangs out the washing, they stand with their back to the wind with the line in front of them. The grass is continuously trampled at a precise distance upwind of the line and is kept short as a result. The clover is a poor competitor but is able to grow where the trampling keeps the grass in check. That's all it takes to make the pattern on the lawn.

Competition between species is affected by the slightest of things – often by the most unexpected things. For example, increase the amount of zinc in the soil by just a tiny fraction and you change everything. If you find yourself on the A939 east of Tomintoul, look at the ground underneath the transmission pylons crossing the Lecht Pass. Where rainwater drips down from the galvanised metal you will find an extensive cover of lichen, strips of which extend down the hillside where the legs of the pylons touch the ground.

Close to our house is an old iron fencepost set into rock. It is bent-over slightly from the vertical. Rain water runs down the post carrying dissolved iron onto the rock. The result is a dark band on the surface containing a few iron-tolerant lichens. But the top of this post happens to be a favourite lookout perch for birds and if you trace the line vertically downwards from this perch, you find a patch of mustard-yellow lichen that is thriving on the bird droppings.

If the rock is volcanic and silica-rich, and therefore acidic, and it happens to be near the sea, and is influenced by salt spray, then the yellow lichens will almost certainly be *Candelariella*, which has a bumpy surface like a cauliflower when viewed under a hand lens. But if it is inland and it happens to be on limestone, the bird droppings will create a yellow patch consisting mostly of *Xanthoria*, which takes the form of a leafy rosette.

That's the exciting thing about lichen. Because it is in direct contact with the surface, it can tell you lots of things about the chemistry of that surface …

In front of you at the head of Loch Slapin is Clach Oscar. It's a favourite lookout perch for crows. Look closely. Notice the bones of dead voles on its flat top; the bird pellets, the streaks of lime down the sides. This isn't just a rock. This is a bird's dining table; an oasis of nitrogen; a fertile island in a sea of granite. And the result? A forest of lichen, attached to the rock by an umbilical cord. It is as if the rock is giving birth and coming alive with this extraordinary growth.

You could imagine David Attenborough sitting here … a slow wave of the hand only, to indicate what is behind him, but no sudden movements, so as not to cause a disturbance … and then, turning his head slowly to camera, he would whisper, in that characteristic measured voice that he would always use when describing a mountain gorilla or a Komodo Dragon … he would whisper:

"Rock Tripe – *Lasallia pustulata*"

And we would be spellbound.

There are certain places that you wouldn't want to graze a cow. Lead mines and the once-green arable land that is now pockmarked with overgrown spoil heaps are examples. So much concern has been shown about lead entering the food chain via grazing animals that farmers were encouraged to remove the toxic waste from their land.

Forty years later the same farmers are being paid not to remove the spoil heaps. The sites are now regarded as ecologically and internationally important. The lead waste supports a rare community of plants that are known to ecologists by such mysterious code names as 'OV37', 'calaminarian grassland' and 'metallophytes'. There are four key species – the mountain pansy, alpine penny-cress, Pyrenean scurvygrass and spring sandwort, a plant so at home on lead, it is also known as 'leadwort'. In laboratory studies, some of these plants actually grow more quickly when lead and zinc have been added to the soil.

In the north-west of Scotland, these particular metallophytes are rare. Alpine penny-cress can still be found on Rum and there are past records of spring sandwort growing on Mull, and at a disused lead mine near Strontian. Mountain pansy used to be recorded in North Uist, but recent reports of Pyrenean scurvygrass found in Skye have yet to be confirmed by DNA analysis.

There is, however, an extensive list of 'easier' plants that have been associated with metal spoil heaps. These include kidney vetch, autumn gentian, fragrant orchid, frog orchid, meadow oat-grass, moonwort, grass of Parnassus, carline thistle and mossy saxifrage. It is interesting to note that in this part of Scotland, these plants are almost always found on basic rocks, usually limestone.

Mountain bikes and trial bikes are often regarded negatively by conservationists, but in some cases they can actually give plants a helping hand.

The rare Pyrenean scurvygrass is one example. In the Peak District in England, it has been found to survive best on ground that is regularly disturbed by walkers and cyclists.

A similar paradox is provided by footpaths. Hill walking wears away the soil and can lead to serious erosion on popular routes. But in flatter grassland areas, the gently-trampled path is often the best place to look for those rare dwarf plants that cannot compete with taller species.

From bird lime to spoil heaps; from galvanised pylons to human trampling – it's an ill wind that blows nobody good.

NATURE'S WAY OF CELEBRATING VICTORY

The Olympic games sheds more light on the nature-nurture debate

I have difficulty these days watching tennis on TV. All that grunting and shouting makes me instantly reach for the mute button. And then there is all the clenching of fists and punching the air after winning a point. I blame it on Margaret Thatcher and the unbridled individualism of the eighties.

And so I watched the Olympics with trepidation. As expected, Nadal pumped up his biceps after every point. Mind you, if I had biceps like Nadal, I'd do that too. But horror of horrors: the clenched fist was appearing everywhere, even in the ice-cold discipline of gymnastics. What was going on?

Recent research has suggested that such in-your-face celebrations are not just a sign of the times. Photographs of blind judo contestants at the Paralympic Games in 2004 showed them raising their arms in a clenched fist salute after victory, just like their sighted counterparts. The contestants had been blind from birth and so they couldn't have been following some cultural trend by copying what everyone else was doing. These gestures could not have been learned by visual means, and it has been suggested that something far more deep-seated is involved.

The same research highlights some interesting cultural traits. Athletes from cultures that are regarded as 'individualistic', like the US and Britain, tend to hide their disappointment when they lose, compared with 'less-individualistic' cultures where disappointment is more openly expressed. This is a very dubious form of labelling, but if we broadly accept the idea, the research shows that blind-from-birth athletes react to defeat like athletes from less-individualistic cultures – bowing their heads and slumping their shoulders. They let their natural emotions show, or to put it another way, they haven't experienced the cultural pressure to keep them bottled up.

This opens the perennial debate about behaviour – whether it is learned or innate. We always fall into the same trap – it has to be either one or the other. We like our explanations to be simple.

But behaviour isn't simple. Song birds have a basic alarm call that seems to be hard-wired, but they have to hear other song birds performing before they can develop their full operatic score. Footballers may have a basic pattern of celebration involving a raised arm or two but that is modified by learning from your club mates what is acceptable in a given time and place.

During the World Cup in 1966, you were allowed a small skip in the air if you scored a goal from 25-yards-out. Nowadays you have to celebrate by performing four backward somersaults with two and a half twists. And if you have just become a father – the whole team is expected to join you in a display of 'synchronised-cradle-rocking'.

There are many difficulties when comparing the behaviour of humans with other animals. We have a complex range of emotions that may or may not be peculiarly human. Do other animals feel 'pride' in the same way that we do? Are we to compare a gorilla beating its chest with a gold medal winner raising his arms on the victory rostrum? Do rival blackbirds have a sense of 'fair play', like the boxer who stops short his attack when an opponent goes down, or do the birds react automatically to an 'appeasement posture'?

This is one area of enquiry where research workers are becoming increasingly wound-up and serious. Two camps oppose each other, separated by 30 years of changing attitudes. On one side there are psychologists that say humans are uniquely human and anthropomorphism went out with Walt Disney. On the other side there are those that say we are not so special after all, and that other animals share with us the ability to make tools, use language, have morals and exhibit emotions. Neither side is as objective as their scientific training should have told them to be.

Take emotions. Elephants have been described as showing 'empathy'

Sequence showing rival male blackbirds competing for territory. The lower bird
exhibits an 'appeasement posture', the head lowered signalling defeat before
taking flight. The victor 'celebrates', tail erect in triumphal display

by sharing the emotional pain of a crippled herd member. A humpback
whale has been described as showing 'gratitude' for being disentangled
from a crab line. Magpies have been described as performing funeral
rites for a dead companion, suggesting 'grief'. There are reports of ravens
'falling in love' and of dogs having a 'moral sense' of right and wrong.
Flatworms have been described as exhibiting 'anxiety' when they have to
risk an electric shock in order to feed. Chimpanzees that were seen dancing
in front of a waterfall have been reported as experiencing a sense of 'awe
and wonder'. A baboon urinating on a rival has been interpreted as showing
'revenge'.

All these animals are special. Do we have to force the issue by giving
them human characteristics? They aren't second-rate humans. They are
first-rate animals in their own right. Whales and other cetaceans can
communicate under water in a far more sophisticated manner than we
can. Magpies and other birds can fly by flapping their arms – that's pretty
special! Bats use echo location. Pigeons, eels and salmon have a built-in
compass. *Homo sapiens* can look backwards and forwards in time with
all the problems and benefits that come from an introspective brain. That's
special too.

But perhaps we are taking these comparisons too seriously. This debate
is in need of some much-needed relief. Take snakes. When two rival

males compete for a female, the vanquished beast will slink away into the undergrowth and remain sexually inactive for several weeks. The victor will 'celebrate' his success by instantly mating with his prize. Which brings to mind an entry in the Duchess of Marlborough's diary:

"My lord returned from the war today and pleasured me twice in his top boots."

The Natural History of a Peat Bog

A SHORT WALK ACROSS THE MOOR

*Carnivorous plants and exotic birds
on a Scottish peat bog in spring*

Wildlife enthusiasts often ask when is the best time to visit north-west Scotland. It has to be the first half of June: long days, not so many midges, spring flowers giving way to summer flowers and birdlife at its best.

Take a walk out across the moorland just now – any boggy peat moorland will do. Don't set off at Naismith's pace. Three miles per hour is far too fast for this, but just take your time to see what is actually growing and what you are walking over. Wear wellies. Bring walking poles if you must. I personally wonder how we managed before they were invented and were told that we need them even when walking on the road, like cross-country skiers without skis. "What's wrong with a walking stick?" I ask. But then as Janet keeps telling me – some people are helped by having two sticks. But I still can't understand the walkers who arrived at our house the other week with a car-boot-full of the things. I thought they'd arrived to sweep the chimney.

Whichever peat moorland you choose for your walk, it will be fed by one of the highest rainfalls in the British Isles and as such is one of the most mineral-deficient habitats. Minerals, trace elements, phosphates, nitrates – all the things you want in a soil for growing livestock and plants – are almost all entirely washed out.

In order to survive in this habitat, the plants have had to resort to some special tactics. To make up for the shortfall in their diet, some of them have become carnivorous.

Look closely amongst the wettest parts of the bog, along the side of hollows and runnels. Here you will find the insect-eaters: plants that look like pale-green starfish that are just this week starting to produce their violet flowers. Common butterwort, *Pinguicula vulgaris*, acts like a natural fly-paper that dissolves insects on contact.

Take a step further to that raised cushion of red sphagnum and you find small rosettes of red leaves covered in sticky tentacles (looking a bit like an old-fashioned hairbrush). This is another insect-eater called sundew, *Drosera rotundifolia*. The plant actually moves after trapping a fly. Very slowly the tentacles appear to curl around the unfortunate victim, which begins to dissolve in a matter of hours.

Drop a small piece of cheese on the leaf. Any cheese will do. (I personally prefer a nice moist Camembert that has been kept out of the fridge for at least two weeks.) The protein in the cheese fools the plant into thinking it has caught a fly and causes the tentacles to curl over and embrace its kill.

Almost everyone who sees a sundew for the first time remarks on how small it is. An average-sized plant would fit under a two-pence coin. It surprises us because we expect something that is carnivorous to be big and to be snapping at our ankles.

Now walk further into the wet, along the edge of that trembling hollow filled with water. Breaking through the surface is bogbean, *Menyanthes trifoliata*. The three leaves on the end of a thick stem resemble a young bean shoot. During the second week in June it is starting to form its flowers. Has there ever been a more-beautiful flower with such an unpromising name? Here amongst the dark peaty water on the bleakest part of the moor you find a dazzling flower: the most-delicate white lace tinged with pink.

Before leaving these peaty pools, it is worth taking a closer look at the water. There is a rainbow layer of colours floating on the surface. The tractor's been leaking oil again? But it hasn't because it isn't oil. To understand what is going on here, we need to look at the chemistry of a peat bog. It seems that the real, culprit is iron.

Iron is doing all sorts of things inside a peat bog. Sometimes it seeps out as rust-coloured patches; sometimes it is concentrated and forms bog iron ore; and sometimes it floats on the surface as a mono-molecular layer, as thin as oil, producing an oil-like diffraction pattern. The thinner the film, the more intense the colour.

Here in the West Highlands, the moor is characterised by three heathers: bell heather (*Erica cinerea*), cross-leaved heath (*Erica tetralix*) and the one that most people associate with Scotland, the one that is sometimes called 'ling' (*Calluna vulgaris*).

Ling sometimes produces white flowers – lucky white heather. Cross-leaved heath can also form white flowers but the cause would seem to be environmental rather than genetic. Look closely at its cluster of swollen pink flowers. Turn it upside down and you will find they are paler underneath. Why?

If you find a plant where there has been peat-cutting, where it has been covered with a lump of peat, a flower can sometimes be found that is almost white. The pink colour develops with exposure to sunlight. Without sun, the pigment doesn't form.

The three heathers are found in quite different parts of the peat moor. It makes an interesting study to describe this using the language of competition. Ling grows where it wants to grow, in soil that is not too wet and not too dry. But cross-leaved heath and bell heather are pushed out to the extremes – into the wet and dry respectively.

The key to this distribution is iron. On a peat moor with a high rainfall, iron accumulates in the waterlogged hollows. Cross-leaved heath grows in the wet because it can tolerate iron. Bell heather avoids the wet because even a small amount of iron will kill it.

If you buy these heathers or their hybrids from a garden centre, all of them will thrive in separate pots filled with medium-moist soil. A heather border can easily be managed to show the different plants growing side by side. But that isn't natural. Put them all together and leave them to compete on undulating ground and the pattern you see in the wild will slowly begin to emerge.

Stand here a while surrounded by the heather and peat. You are about to meet a true icon of the Highlands and Islands. This is the perfect time of year for hearing and seeing divers flying overhead. The 'black-throat' nests on large isolated lochs and lochans. The 'red-throat' favours the smaller lochans as it doesn't need such a long runway to take off and land.

In North America they are called loons. In Scotland, they are divers. Their country name is 'the rain goose' because they quack like a goose and were thought to bring the rain. There is some logic here as they are mostly seen and heard overland when it's wet and misty. When it's clear, they are feeding out at sea.

My favourite is the smaller red-throated diver, *Gavia stellata*, – flying fast overhead: "Quack … quack … quack … quack-quack-quack-quack-quack…" – looking like a flying coat-hanger. It has to be one of the most beautiful birds in Scotland. I call it the 'Page Three Bird' – it always seems to be on page three of the bird book!

You'll need the binoculars for this: burgundy-red throat, silver and black stripes down the back of its neck, pure white underneath, a bright red eye, a slight suggestion of an upturned beak, swims under water for half a minute before resurfacing 30 feet away, legs far back on body, looking a bit like *Hesperornis regalis* (an extinct bird from the Cretaceous) as it shuffles onto its nest hardly able to walk – and that's its problem – it can hardly walk.

What price beauty?

THE ADVENTURE OF THE INNOCENT ASPHODEL

A Sherlock Holmes mystery involving a yellow flower,
a waterlogged peat bog and a cow with a broken leg

There were problems on the peat moor. Cows had been found with their legs broken.

"Devilish business this, Holmes. Who could be doing such a thing?"

"This is not the work of a particular person, Watson. It is too widespread for that. No, my friend, there is something more subtle at work going on here."

"But what could be strong enough to break the leg of a cow?"

"Let us examine the evidence on the ground before jumping to any conclusions."

And so our two companions approach the scene of the crime ...

"The cow was found just here, Watson, at the side of this wet hollow. Do you notice anything unusual about the ground?"

"Only that it is very wet, and there are lots of yellow flowers everywhere."

"Exactly, my friend – that's what everyone sees when they find such a distressed animal. The cows are almost always found alongside these yellow flowers."

"But surely a flower couldn't have done this?"

"Apparently so – that's exactly what is being blamed – a simple yellow flower from the family Liliaceae. It is known as bog asphodel, although some people are so sure of its guilt, they have taken to calling it 'the bone breaker'!"

"But this has to be pure superstition, Holmes. Surely no one of a serious scientific mind would accept that?"

"It's not that simple, Watson. The reputation of the plant has even reached learned circles where it is known by the scientific name *Narthecium ossifragum*, from the Latin word *os* meaning 'bone' and *frangere* 'to break'."

"Well, Holmes, the only scientific explanation I can think of is that when the plant is ingested it must somehow cause the animal to develop a weakness in the bone which then breaks when put under stress."

"I can see how this might appeal to you as a medical man, Watson – some chemical imbalance that removes calcium from the bones, as may occur in some of your elderly patients. But in this particular case, the effect is not so direct. We need to stand back and look at the broader picture.

"Here is a plant that grows only on acid soil. But more relevant to our case – it will only grow on soil where there is a shortage of calcium! The cows that graze exclusively on this type of land are likely to develop a poor bone structure because of the lack of calcium in their diet. On sinking into the wet peat they break their legs trying to get out."

"It seems the puzzle is finally solved, Holmes."

"Not quite, Watson – why, for instance, should this particular plant have been blamed? Why not one of the other flowers? Why not the cross-leaved heath, or one of the orchids, or lousewort, or even that yellow spearwort over there? They all grow on calcium-deficient soils. They are all around us on this moor and yet they haven't been blamed. Why single out the bog asphodel?"

"Perhaps most of the incidents occur from mid to late summer, when the rainfall is heaviest and the ground is at its wettest, and that is just the time when the asphodel is in full flower. It is a striking yellow colour. Perhaps over time, farmers noticed that the cow with the broken leg was always found laid down next to this particular yellow flower."

"Excellent, Watson! And you have the timing of events more or less right. But there is another factor that has contributed to this plant's reputation which involves the way it spreads its seeds."

"I don't follow you, Holmes."

"Well, take a close look at the ground in front of you. Do you notice anything unusual about the position of this plant?"

"Only that it seems to grow along the edge of these pools."

"Exactly, my dear friend! It grows in lines at several levels around each pool.

More generally, it is found on the boundary of a wet hollow and the bank that forms the edge – the very place where a cow would get into difficulties."

"But why should it grow in this particular pattern, Holmes?"

"That, my dear friend, is the key to this riddle! Take a closer look at the flower. Notice the way the seeds are beginning to develop. They are relatively large and are shaped somewhat like a boat. Some are dispersed by the wind but because of their size and weight, many of them land in these pools and drift like a boat across the surface. They drift to the side, and where they beach themselves, that is where they take root.

"Look at the edge of this particular hollow, Watson. See how the plants are distributed – forming lines like tide lines, indicating the water-levels reached throughout July and August when the seeds are shed. You will also note that the prevailing winds are south-westerly and this has concentrated most of the plants along the north-east bank."

"You astonish me, Holmes!"

"Elementary, my dear Watson! There is no villainy here – just a plant that enjoys a high rainfall and a lack of minerals in the soil. Its method of seed dispersal effectively concentrates its flowers in concentric bands around the pools of water – just the place where a cow would sink in – just the place where the farmer would notice the lines of yellow – and the innocent bog asphodel got the blame!"

WHY DO MIDGES BITE SOME PEOPLE AND NOT OTHERS?

A look at the science behind the folklore
with practical suggestions to avoid being bitten

What attracts a biting fly? Why are some people more vulnerable than others? More to the point – how do you stop them biting?

After thousands of laboratory studies and field trials conducted by the American armed forces, university departments, entrepreneurs and pharmaceutical companies, you would think someone would have found an answer.

To this end, research workers have put their arms inside cages full of hungry mosquitoes and compared the attractiveness of their skin before and after it was artificially cooled or warmed; robots have been fitted with clothes soaked in human sweat to compare them with robots wearing clothes soaked in water; goats have been compared with rabbits; turkeys have been compared with chickens; guinea pigs have been fitted with 'gas masks' to remove their expired air and compared with guinea pigs allowed to breathe normally …

The result is a mishmash of contradictions. All the possible factors that might attract a fly to its target have been considered: colour, temperature, scent, carbon dioxide, movement, size, and shape. Take colour, for example. Many experiments found that biting flies prefer to land on dark-coloured objects. But then, when the target was two-dimensional they preferred white.

Some studies have concentrated on airborne scents. Every possible chemical emanating from every possible orifice has been painstakingly investigated – sex hormones, lactic acid, sweat, urine and many other unspeakable things have been examined. You have to know what attracts a midge to have a chance of repelling it.

But things are never that simple. Insect behaviour is fundamentally different from our own behaviour and that of other mammals. Insects don't act like sniffer dogs. They don't simply follow a trail of scent. Male cabbage looper moths, for example, are 'attracted' to female moths. How? The females release a chemical scent but the males don't follow it. Instead, the scent activates the males making them more sensitive to light, whilst at the same time, causing them to fly up-wind. Since the odour from the female will drift down-wind, a male activated by the chemical will soon find its target.

Mosquitoes and midges may do the same thing. Their flight towards a source of carbon dioxide (such as a person's breath) may not involve simply following a chemical gradient. The carbon dioxide may trigger a response to fly into the wind.

Insects tend to fly at a preferred height which is affected by wind speed. The stronger the wind, the lower they fly until they are finally grounded. But it's not just a matter of having a preferred air speed determined by the aerodynamics of the wing as in an aeroplane. Their flight behaviour depends on a peculiar feature of the insect eye and brain. Some insects prefer images to move across their eyes from front to back and at a certain speed. The mechanism acts like an autopilot. If they fly sideways, off-course, they turn back into the wind to produce the 'preferred image direction' across the eye. If they fly too close to the ground, the images will rush across their eyes too quickly and they compensate by gaining more height. These are not simple creatures. We are dealing with complex flying machines.

The Scottish Tourist Board would love to have some practical answers to combat the midge, and the zoology departments of Scottish universities have been trying to provide those answers since the 1950s. But over 50 years of research has produced very few new leads.

Where does this leave those of us who have to work outdoors? Midge hoods made from fine-gauge netting can be effective, especially when working in the garden for short periods. But they may be restrictive in certain occupations and for all-day use.

Most people find themselves relying on insect repellants that are applied to the skin, but these often depend on an unpleasant chemical known as DEET (diethyltoluamide). The SAS have gone one better and have taken a lead from the local forestry workers. They smother themselves in a certain brand of skin softener. They swear by it. Butch, elite troops are crawling at this very moment through wet undergrowth, fully midge-proofed, with the added confidence of knowing that, at the end of a hard day's training, their skin will remain beautifully soft.

Where does it leave the camper, on holiday, arriving on a perfect evening at an idyllic spot on the shore of Loch Hope, surrounded by trees and bracken, a slight breeze blowing; isn't this just perfect? And then at three in the morning, when the wind drops, being woken up, breathing them in, up your nose, in your hair and ears, biting your eyelids ... and in desperation you pull on a pair of ladies' tights, like a bank robber and get out of the tent, into the car, and drive away as quickly as possible with all the windows wide open, and head for Inverness …

You have to have experienced a massed midge-attack first-hand to appreciate the sheer horror.

But all is not lost. A number of courses of action have been tried in the battle to overcome the midge:

As well as surface repellants, there have been claims (uncorroborated) for the effectiveness of 'systemic repellants' which includes taking extra doses of vitamin B.

Carbon dioxide has been used as bait with some success. The released gas causes midges to fly into the wind to meet whatever fate is there to greet them.

The more flies that have settled on your skin, the more likely you are to attract other flies. It is known as 'the invitation effect'. By the same principle, mirrored surfaces have also been found to attract more flies.

So there you have it. The answer's simple: smother yourself in Marmite, avoid breathing out, and don't go anywhere near a mirror!

THE SECRET LIFE OF A DRAGONFLY

The peculiar nature of dragonfly flight
in the light of recent studies on aerodynamics

A Hungarian athlete had an idea. In the quest to throw a javelin further than anyone else, he took a hammer and made a series of dents in the once-smooth surface. Miklos Nemèth designed a javelin that flew so far, it was a danger to spectators and the model was eventually banned from competitive athletics.

All this sounds very odd and counterintuitive. You would think that the smoother the surface, the more streamlined it would become and the further it would travel. That may hold true for a bullet or a supersonic jet, but when it comes to slower speeds, that all gets turned on its head. Take a golf ball. The reason it is covered in dimples is not just to provide better grip when hit. The rough surface causes it to fly further.

I've gone off on a bit of a tangent here. I'm supposed to be talking about the aerodynamics of dragonfly wings ...

Three hundred million years ago, dragonfly-like insects ruled the skies with wingspans of over half a metre. They are still with us today in the form of dragonflies and damselflies, but not quite that big. True dragonflies hold their resting wings out at the side whilst the damselflies hold them in line with the body. The wings move independently of each other which makes them highly manoeuvrable. The lack of synchronisation also causes them to clash together and produce a loud rustling noise.

Their slow flapping action can propel a large dragonfly to speeds of up to 50 kilometres per hour. Some can glide for periods of half a minute without a wingbeat. How can they do that?

If the wing is to delay stalling, the air moving across its surface must stay in close contact. If the smooth flow of air can be broken to form a layer of tiny ripples, these are less likely to break away or 'separate' from the surface. Aeronautical engineers call this a 'turbulent boundary layer'. (Paradoxically, this also reduces the overall drag: hence the golf ball's dimples and the roughened surface of Nemèth's javelin.)

If you look closely at a dragonfly's wing, you see a pattern of veins raised above the surface. This has long been known to provide longitudinal stiffening, but recent research shows that the veins can also produce a turbulent boundary layer capable of generating the extra lift needed for gliding flight.

Aero-modellers create this effect by gluing a raised cotton thread along the leading edge of a model wing. Bats do it by having their finger bones project above the stretched wing surface, like the ribs in an umbrella. Birds of prey and herons do it by sticking out their thumb in a structure called the 'bastard wing'. And sports cars do something similar with a 'spoiler' in the quest to reduce drag.

There are many features that make the dragonfly's wing special. The wing muscles are like our muscles. They contract when a nerve tells them to contract, unlike other flies whose muscles respond automatically to vibrations. If a dragonfly damages a wing or has part of it removed, it can still fly by maintaining a constant wingbeat. This is quite different from other flies whose wingbeat rhythm depends on the mechanical resonance of the wings. When an ordinary fly loses part of its wing, its beat frequency goes haywire.

And then there is the way the dragonflies mate: not end-to-end like any normal fly, no, – the male first transfers his sperm into a special pocket between his second and third segment. He then grabs the female just behind the neck with the tip of his abdomen. The female bends her body to reach the 'sperm pocket', and the two take up a position known as a 'mating wheel'.

[Don't even think about it.] – Janet.

Once mating is completed, the female will fly off to lay her eggs in a quiet stretch of water or insert them into a plant leaf. The egg develops into a predatory nymph which spends its time hunting for whatever passes by – another dragonfly nymph, a tadpole, a water beetle, or even a small fish – and then as soon as it is within range it shoots out a special weapon called the mask that is hinged at one end and armed with claws at the other, grabbing the victim and transferring it to its mouth. You may have seen something like it in the film *Alien*.

In some species this aquatic phase can continue for up to five years. I remember a peaty pool behind our house. It was mid-summer, early morning; a perfect sunny day with no wind. Out from the surface crawled the black oily-looking grub with the complicated mouth. It stayed attached to a leaf of sedge and then miraculously, over a period of an hour, it split open and out came the pale adult with its crumpled wings. Minutes later, the wings were inflated, and the creature turned into a dragonfly.

This same ritual has been taking place unaltered for over 200 million years. Fossil dragonflies found in ancient sediments look just the same as those found on the moor today. Darwinian evolution is slow. When you have a good design that functions well, there is no need to change it.

A Hebridean Slant on Life

IN SEARCH OF THE ELUSIVE 'RIVER OTTER'

When is a Scottish otter not a sea otter?
Examining the evidence and uncovering the true nature of the beast

Which furry animal lives in rivers and the sea off the west coast of Scotland and catches fish? Answer: the Eurasian otter.

It's quite simple really…

"So that will be a sea otter?"

"No. It's not the sea otter. That's a completely different beast – found on the west coast of North America, floating on its back and cracking crabs with a rock that it keeps in a pouch under its armpit."

"So it's a river otter then?"

"Yes."

"Like Gavin Maxwell's first otter that he once kept in a bath?"

"No – that isn't a river otter. That's the 'smooth-coated otter' from Iraq and Asia that lives in rivers and the sea."

"But why isn't that called a river otter if it lives in rivers?"

"Because it lives in the sea as well."

"But why do we call our Scottish otter a river otter if it lives in the sea as well?"

It should be simple, but it isn't.

Back in 1968 there were 19 species and 63 sub-species of otter. By 1978, the numbers had been rationalised to just nine species whilst in 2007, the tally had risen to 13.

Of the three species that are called 'river otters', none are to be found exclusively in rivers, but are quite happy in the sea. Eight of the remaining species also live in rivers but they are not called river otters. Two species are found in the sea and yet only one species is called a 'sea otter' (the other is called a 'sea cat').

Perhaps it's time to stop classifying these animals by habitat and drop the words 'river otter' and 'sea otter' completely. The otter we see in Scotland is the 'Eurasian otter' with the scientific name *Lutra lutra*. And that's that.

Unless you happen to be in Shetland, you don't regularly see them during the day, and yet there are signs everywhere. Follow a quiet stretch of river or coast and you will find 'spraints' or otter droppings. They can often be found where there is a prominent landmark such as a bend in a river or a partly submerged rock, or under a bridge.

The signs are there but you need to know how to read them. On bare rock, look for streaks of green algae. On grass, look for patches that are slightly darker than the surrounding area, often growing on a low mound. If otters have been here recently, these sites will be covered in spraints, containing scattered fragments of bone weathering-out from a shiny black groundmass. Smell it. It has a distinctly fishy smell. These animals belong to the same family as skunks and communicate by scent.

Look closely at a spraint and poke it with a stick. It is August and you should find fish scales, the jawbones of frog, backbones of eel, bits of crab shell and the occasional bird bone. (I keep looking for bits of Simon King but no luck so far.) In winter there may be rabbit fur and rabbit vertebrae to add to the list. This otter has the pick of what it wants to eat. It is at the top of the food chain with no enemies except man.

The grass at a sprainting site is dark green because of the phosphates and nitrates. It grows more quickly than the surrounding turf and is often left ungrazed at one specific spot. (Perhaps the sheep are put off by the strong scent.) When this taller grass dies back in winter, it creates a mound of decaying humus. Some of these mounds can be over six inches high,

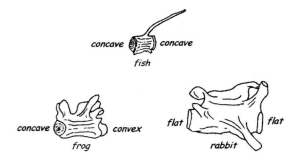

Vertebrae found in otter spraints

signifying years of continuous use by generations of otters.

Almost everyone is surprised by the contents of a spraint. As a quick guide to what an otter has been eating, look for bits of backbone – the individual vertebrae. Examine the main articulating surface (the centrum) where the bones fit together. Those with two concave sides are from a fish; one concave and one convex side indicate a frog; two flat sides indicate a rabbit. What a life! If it wants a rabbit, it just goes down a hole and takes one. If it wants some sport it catches an eel.

Radio telemetry and careful tracking have shown that male otters can cover great distances. Some studies have recorded them travelling up to ten miles in a single night. On Skye, I have found spraints from sea-level to almost 1000 feet along the cliff edges of Dunvegan Head. This otter is the master of coast, river and crag.

So how do you spot an otter? First, you have to select a quiet section of coastline where you have identified some fresh sprainting sites. Go early morning at first light, or late evening. Wash off any aftershave or scent and wear drab non-rustle clothing. Find a spot down-wind of your chosen site and sit perfectly still without making any noise. If you have no luck after an hour, go back to bed.

In all my time of watching otters in Skye, there have been only a few occasions when I could predict where I could find them – when I discovered a holt occupied by a female with cubs. That was special. Each evening for a number of weeks, the mother would appear 15 minutes after the sun had gone down, after the shadow of the hill had crossed the entrance. And then the three cubs would appear all at once and everyone was happy.

But mostly they are chance encounters or you have to content yourself with discovering their tracks and signs. As well as the usual spraints, otters leave a very distinct five-clawed webbed footprint in soft mud, sand or snow. They make 'slides' in snow. They wear the grass away along the side of small streams to leave prominent tracks between their sprainting mounds. And they leave the skins of rabbits turned inside-out like a wet rubber glove. Foxes will also do this but otters do it differently. They take their rabbits to water to eat. Many times have I found the empty skin of a rabbit left along the edge of an inland pool, or part-floating on the shore of a freshwater loch.

Furry animal with appealing eyes? Try telling that to the rabbit!

KELP, TIDES AND ILLUSIONS
IN THE SOUND OF HARRIS

Why is this gap in the Outer Isles described as
'remarkable' in the West Coast Pilot and what makes
the region's Admiralty Charts unique?

I have in front of me the Admiralty Chart for the Sound of Harris – scale 1:20 000. But something isn't right. The magnetic north doesn't point to the top of the map. It has been turned diagonally to face north-west.

As far as I know, this is the only Admiralty Chart in the world where you find magnetic north turned on its side. No ordinary stretch of sea: this gap in the Outer Isles, this inspiration for a poem (*Sound of Harris* by Ian Stephen, the coastguard officer from Lewis), this slalom course of marker buoys from Berneray to Leverburgh.

It has to be worth a closer look. And so I open out the chart and put on my reading glasses ... and find some strange symbols midway between Killegray and Cope Passage. It looks like the dead branch of a tree floating in the water. I quickly turn to the Symbols and Abbreviations used on Admiralty Charts, expecting to find something like 'Here, great quantity of driftwood can be found'. But no such luck. Instead, on page 27, I find a list describing the 'Nature of the Seabed' and the driftwood symbol turns out to be 'Kelp'.

Fascinated at finding seaweed marked on a shipping chart, I look elsewhere on adjacent charts, but fail to find it marked in the same concentration.

What makes the Sound of Harris different? Why the need to indicate kelp in such a specific way as a shipping hazard? Even more surprising – the kelp fronds are drawn floating in a specific orientation, mostly following a westerly flow. The map actually shows the orientation of the fronds drawn out by the water currents!

This is where biology comes in. Kelp grows faster in a steady flow of water. The fronds are kept separated and so the optimum surface area is exposed for photosynthesis to occur, resulting in optimum growth. But then it gets complicated. Why do we find such conditions in the Sound of Harris?

In desperation I turn to the *West Coast of Scotland Pilot*. This is a weighty tome, the essential reference for any navigator of these waters, each line formally numbered from one to seventy on each page. And yet I find that even this dry text gets excited whenever the Sound of Harris is mentioned. I cut straight to the words in bold: 'Tidal Streams' (page 37, lines 28-55). I discover that in the channels between Ensay and Killegray, the streams are described as 'remarkable'.

The conservative Pilot does not use such terms lightly. It goes on to describe how the 'spring tides' flow to the south-east as the tide rises, and then reverses, flowing north-west as the tide falls. ('Spring' has nothing to do with springtime but describes the tides when the sun and moon are pulling together in the same direction.) Then, during 'neap tides' (when the sun and moon are pulling in adjacent directions), the flow is south-east during the daytime and reverses south-west during the night. But this only applies in summer. In winter, the neap tides run north-west during daytime and creep back in south-eastwards during the night (presumably when nobody is looking).

For a navigator in this stretch of water, this is no joke. And it gets even more serious when you read that the speed of these tidal steams can reach five knots!

To try and make sense of all this, you need to stand back and imagine the sea level rising in response to the gravitational pull of the sun and moon. It follows the path of a giant wave travelling up the west coast of Scotland, dividing unevenly as it travels along each side of the Outer Hebrides. It squeezes through the Little Minch and pours around the top of Lewis to pile up on the west side. There is only one place where it can break though back into the Minch – the Sound of Harris. But don't ask me to explain why it reverses when the sun goes down and why it's different in winter – I'm only a biologist, and understanding seaweed is hard enough!

Whilst on the topic of seaweed, and kelp in particular, now is a good time to make the most of the next low tide to explore the lower shore. Look carefully amongst the fronds of kelp for a tiny limpet that feeds on its surface. This is the blue-rayed limpet, *Patina pellucida*. It's about the size of the nail on your little finger. The surface is marked by four parallel lines as if drawn with a fluorescent marker pen – a stunning electric blue – making this one of the most beautiful objects to be found on the sea shore.

From the shore on north Skye, I look across the Little Minch. I can see the gap between North Uist and Harris and the flattened cone of Pabbay beyond. The hillsides slope gently down into the shallow waters with their hidden reefs. Good for kelp. Good for limpets. No wonder the ferryboat is flat-bottomed.

On certain days, when conditions are calm and the air is cold, it all looks so different. The base of the hillsides curve back underneath themselves and appear reflected, mirror-like, upside-down in the sea. A mirage!

On a different day when the air is warm, the air settles in distinct layers of different densities stacked above the sea surface. When this happens, the Sound of Harris takes the form of an enclosed portal – like a magical gateway through a wall of shimmering rock.

The edges of the hillsides suddenly rear upwards to form an upside-down image floating in the sky. Pabbay is joined as if by a wisp of smoke to its inverted cone. The Sound of Harris now frames one of the world's great illusions – the superior mirage or Fata Morgana.

We take so much of what we see for granted. The familiar skyline barely gets a second glance: "Harris looks a bit strange today," we say. "Must be the weather."

Life goes on. The flat-bottomed ferry plies its trade. The fisherman checks his creels. The B&B landlady waves her guests goodbye. And all the while, the Sound of Harris continues to be what it has always been – 'remarkable'.

THE CURIOUS CASE OF THE
LEFT-HANDED DITCH DIGGER

A celebration of handed-ness in nature from
left-handed sugars to right-handed periwinkles
and how flatfish evolved to lie on their left or right side

Take a crystal of glucose and pass a beam of polarised light through it. The likelihood is that it will have rotated the polarised light to the right and not to the left. Left-handed glucose is bad news. It is called 'laevorotatory' or L-Glucose for short. Your body can't make use of it; neither can most other life-forms on our planet. Life has evolved in this part of the universe to use mostly right-handed sugar – 'dextrorotatory' or

D-Glucose. We call it 'dextrose'.

Our Earth spins on its axis. In the Northern Hemisphere, flowing water will tend to spiral in a clockwise direction. This means that any debris floating down a river will tend to collect along the right bank. The same 'Coriolis force' causes low-pressure weather systems to rotates anti-clockwise over Stornoway and clockwise over Sydney. Whatever the scale, nature turns to the left or to the right. Our galaxy spirals in space; our DNA is composed of two chemical chains wound in a right-handed double helix.

We see spirals everywhere, most noticeably in the shells of snails. Some species of snail spiral to the left. These include the 'sinistral miniature horn shell', the Neptune shell, *Neptunea contraria*, and almost all the snails that belong to a group called the 'clausiliids'. Most of the Scottish snails, especially our marine snails, are right-handed. Take a walk down to the shore and examine the whelks and winkles. The shells can be seen to turn clockwise when viewed from the tip to the opening, following a right-handed spiral (*dextral*). Occasionally, you may get one that turns in the opposite direction (*sinistral*), but these are as rare as Charlie Bucket's golden ticket.

Flatfish have evolved to lie on either their left or their right side. They have eyes that migrate around from underneath to sit on top of the head. In flounders, plaice and halibut, it is the left eye that has migrated upwards. In turbot and brill, it is the right eye that makes the journey. This results in the entire skull becoming rearranged as bones, blood vessels and nerves are twisted to reach the top of the head. Not the most 'intelligent design', but in the competitive world of evolution – needs must.

The horns of cattle, sheep and goats curl in a specific direction. The bark of the sweet chestnut has a characteristic spiral along the trunk. And according to the Flanders and Swan lyric there is 'the right-handed honeysuckle and the left-handed bindweed', sadly never to embrace.

Handed-ness is everywhere. We find it in physics, chemistry, and biology – in the very structure of things. But how much does it occur in animal behaviour?

In our own species, we regard ourselves as either right or left-handed. But what of other animals? Are there left-handed horses that prefer to be approached and mounted from the left side? Are there dextral dogs and sinistral sheep? When gathering sheep, a crofter will favour moving them in a particular direction, either clockwise or anticlockwise. Is this based on the lie of the land, or does it depend on whether the dogs are left or right-handed?

The first time I saw a raven in flight, I couldn't help noticing its habit of turning over on its back in a half-roll. The same raven during any particular spell of watching always turned the same way. Was there such a thing as a left-handed or right-handed raven? You would never see the bird alternate between left and right. The same bird would always roll the same way. For years I was convinced of this. And then I thought: Perhaps it depends on which way the wind is blowing or on which side is facing the sun, or perhaps the bird was waiting until it was safely out of sight when it would flip mockingly the other way!

As for us humans, there's no doubting we use a dominant hand to perform delicate tasks. Sherlock Holmes was always on the lookout for clues that separated right-handed and left-handed suspects:

"Here, Watson, is the work of a left-handed man!"

"What am I looking at, Holmes?"

"Take a closer look at the marshy ground and the way it has been drained."

"But all I see is a mass of hummocks and ridges and the occasional edge of an old peat bog."

"Quite so, Watson. But notice that faint line of shadow snaking its way across the moor. As you look up the slope, the line is marked by an overgrown ditch and a raised bank of heather. The important point, Watson, is that the bank keeps to the *right* of the ditch as you face up the slope!"

"I don't follow you, Holmes."

"Well, if you were digging a ditch here, Watson, which way would you face?"

" I would face uphill to make it easier on the back."

"Exactly, my dear friend – and because you are right-handed, you would throw the earth to your *left!*"

There are many abandoned marshland areas that were once drained like this. All that remains today are the low banks of cleared earth meandering out from the marsh, following the natural drainage lines. November is a good time of year to take a walk over the back of the croft into the drabbest of these landscapes, up onto the saturated peat moor, to try and find these faintest of signs.

The scene is as depressing as it gets. The weather is depressing. The lack of sun at this time of year is even more depressing. So you have nothing to lose, and imagine the excitement of actually finding one of these abandoned drainage channels. You may even find one that was dug by a left-handed man! Don't dismiss this as a sign of Seasonal Affective Disorder. Don't play down the excitement. At this time of year, surrounded by foul weather and featureless peat bogs, we need all the excitement we can get.

TAKE A BREAK FROM CHRISTMAS SHOPPING
AND HEAD FOR THE HILLS

Searching for animal tracks and signs.
Winter invasions of birds and the nature of 'star jelly'

Christmas! It's nearly here again. It's been coming since October. So here's a last gasp chance to recharge the batteries, clear out the sinuses and get some normality back into life.

I recommend a good brisk walk across the moor. This is not meant to be enjoyable – it's too late for that – it's time to steady the mind and get back to reality. Anything but shopping.

Shopping! We were in Edinburgh the other week and were desperate for a mid-morning break. Without thinking, we rushed into a well-known High Street coffee house. You would think it would be simple: "Two cups of coffee please."

"Would that be Mocha, Esperanto, Divertissimo or Café de foie-gras?"

"Just an ordinary cup of coffee with milk please."

"Mini, midi or galacto-bumper?"

"Just an ordinary cup of coffee with milk please."

And then the denouement:

There on the counter appeared two plastic tubs with lids, each lid with a little hole in one end, accompanied by a wooden stick, presumably to stick in the hole, whilst alongside each tub was what looked like a folded brown paper envelope about two-inches-square.

"What's that? I asked, "Sugar?"

The young assistant gave me a disparaging look and slowly explained: "You open it out like so … and then make it into a collar …"

At this point I was tempted to add something along the lines of Bob

Newhart's Walter Raleigh tobacco sketch – 'Don't tell me, Walt … and then, you roll it into a tube and stick it in your ear' – but of course I didn't, and meekly listened as she continued: "… and then, you slide it under the cup so you can carry it without burning your fingers."

There is something terribly challenging in going out in the depths of winter over the drabbest of moors in the foulest of weathers, still hoping to find something of interest. [Some might have other words for it.]

Janet keeps saying I should broaden my horizons and often tells me the Aros Centre in Portree has a good winter programme. But I tell her there is so much to see right here on the doorstep. Imagine … walking along the edge of a burn and for the first time finding bright green patches of grass. You hadn't notice them in summer, but now that the colours on the moor are turning drab and brown, you spot the splash of green immediately.

You see it when you take the shortcut into Dunvegan, just past the campsite. Park the car and take a close look at the river north of the bridge. There are two dark-green patches of grass just up from the water's edge. If you have time to look under the bridge, you will see similar colours on one of the stones standing proud of the water.

You are almost certain to find otter spraints here. Over time, the fertilizing effect of fish bits, rabbit fur and left-over frogs becomes more noticeable. On rock, the surface becomes colonized by fine green algae. On grass, the decaying remains create elevated mounds, indicating centuries of otter activity at the same site.

The same clues are sometimes left by foxes. I remember climbing Bruach na Frithe in winter. On a flat grassy slope, just before the rocky ascent starts to get serious, there is a bright-green patch of grass. In areas of high rainfall like this, soluble nitrates and phosphates are soon leached out of the soil, and any localised replacement has a dramatic effect on the vegetation.

On prominent landmarks you will find similar signs left by birds. Their perching sites will often be covered in different plants. An isolated boulder will have a yellow top, whilst the highest point of a grassy ridge often supports different wild flowers due to the nitrogen-enriched soil and better drainage. It's surprising how many times you find the yellow-flowering lady's bedstraw, growing amongst bird feathers and regurgitated pellets.

Perhaps I really should give the Aros Centre a try.

This year (2008) has been one of the best summers for fruit trees. After waiting for over 20 years, our apple trees finally produced a decent crop of apples, and some of them were actually ripe enough to have brown pips! It has also been an exceptional year for rowan berries, which have been attracting large numbers of birds from Scandinavia. Over 400 waxwings were recorded between the 3rd and 4th November in Portree. One even appeared in our neighbour's garden. There has also been a steady influx of redwings and fieldfares throughout the region.

I was sent an email recently with a link to the BBC Radio Scotland 'Outdoors Team'. It seems that we are under attack from Martians who have been blowing 'slime' over everything. The BBC even produced a weblink with a video and photo gallery of the aforementioned slime that is appearing all across Scotland's countryside. The reporters are mystified. The Royal Botanic Gardens in Edinburgh have confirmed it isn't a plant. The Macaulay Institute in Aberdeen have ruled out fungi. It has apparently been named 'star jelly'.

Earlier this year, *New Scientist* magazine was sent a photograph of some similar slime, and readers were invited to send in suggestions as to what it might be. They were offered £25 for answers that were published.

There is some right now on the top of the hill overlooking our croft: blobs of translucent jelly. I was out there this morning to photograph it. After a severe overnight frost, it was frozen solid and could easily have been mistaken for ice.

By way of explanation, everything from slime mold to Martian mucus has been suggested. But I've always believed it to be the remains of a frog after a predator has finished with it. The contents of the frog's oviduct is left behind and, and on exposure to moisture, the albumen swells up to form the unpalatable jelly – frogspawn without the spawn. Well, that's my answer. And I never did get my £25.

Last-minute Christmas presents are always a problem. What to get the outdoor naturalist who has everything? Here are a few suggestions that might help:

Portable water dispenser for use on the move. These come in several forms. Most resemble the skin of a bloated toad that you slide down the back of your neck. A flexible tube leads to a rubber mouth-piece which you need to bite in order to release the flow. Sucking will not work. Nobody told me this. And when you finally get it to work, it tastes like plasma delivered at body temperature because you've been carrying this thing about all day in the small of your back. Verdict: Highly recommended, especially for Christmas parties.

Deluxe set of seven walking poles. These can be bought in a range of colours and make a splendid present for those who like to take out a different pole each day. They come in their own canvas carrying case and are fully spring-loaded and inter-connectable, enabling them to double-up as drain rods when required. Verdict: Perfect for the active DIY enthusiast.

[Janet has just reminded me that it's Christmas and the season of good will.]

... There is also a High Street version made from tungsten carbide steel — as used in NATO attack aircraft — with polycarbonate hangrips, EVA midsoles and anti-pronation roll bars. The luxury model has an additional foldaway collar in the handle for carrying that all-important cup of coffee whilst on the move.

SEVEN ANNOYING THINGS
AND A NEW YEAR'S RESOLUTION

An end-of-term blast at everything from scientific nomenclature to the woeful state of modern tennis

I couldn't help noticing the starlings the other day. There must have been at least 50 of them sitting on the electric wires like fat clothes pegs on a washing line. Each bird had positioned itself with a gap of six inches between itself and its nearest neighbour. When they took flight, the gap between them remained precise and constant. Animals, especially those that live in groups, are acutely aware of each other and have a sense of personal space.

You park the car in a car park and there's acres of space all around, and yet you can almost guarantee that the next person to arrive will park neatly right next to you with only a two-foot gap to spare. When guests arrive at our B&B I tell them: "There's no one else coming – you have the car park all to yourselves." But it's no use. They continue to park broadside-on and then squeeze between the gap to shake hands. As an experiment, I have taken to driving our car onto the coal heap. But it makes no difference. When they return the next day, there is the car, wheels in the coal, right alongside.

As a biologist, I should regard this as a fascinating scientific phenomenon – an example of comparative psychology and cross-species behaviour. And yet what really gets me, every time I look at it – what really annoys me is that bloomin' dent in the car door.

Janet keeps telling me I should be more tolerant: "We're only human and these things happen". I know these are admirable sentiments and so, what better way to start the New Year? What better New Year's Resolution than to be more tolerant?

If I'm going to be serious about this, I'm going to need help. Someone suggested I might try meditation exercises: "Breathe slowly... feel the air entering the nostrils... and count to three... Now, think of all those things that annoy you."

No – it's no good – I'm sorry – it's not working.

OK, perhaps I should make a list and take them slowly, one by one, in ascending order of annoyance. I'm sitting quite relaxed at the moment... and the first item on the list is:

No.1) Plant and Animal Names.

It was the 18th century Swedish naturalist Carolus Linnaeus who classified organisms using a binomial system – two names, both in Latin. The first or 'generic' name begins with a capital letter, the second or 'specific' name is always written in lower case. And so we get *Tyrannosaurus rex* or *T. rex* for short, written in italics to signify it's in Latin: not 'Tyrannosaurus rex'; not 'Tyrannosaurus Rex'; not 'tyrannosaurus rex'; not 'T Rex' the 70s glamrock band; not 'Trex' the cooking fat. I mean how many ways *are* there of getting it wrong?... So breathe slowly, and it's gone... just let it go...

No.2) The New Way of Speaking used by TV and Radio Sports Presenters.

What does it matter if they say that someone is '25 years of age' instead of '25 years old'; if they keep saying 'at the minute' instead of 'at the moment'; and that Colin Montgomerie is about to reach the 'sicth' green instead of the 'sixth'? Tell yourself it doesn't matter... breathe in... and slowly out... and it really doesn't bother me when a commentator on Radio 5 at the European Swimming Championships says: 'If he finals, he should medal.' It doesn't matter. It's really not important...

[It's all right dear. I'm just clearing my throat...]

No.3) The BBC *Horizon* Programme.

Pure drama – hardly any science. But who needs it? I'm watching too much telly anyway.

No.4) The Size of Modern Tennis Rackets.

I saw a photograph of some contortionist the other day who had this trick of fitting his body inside two unstrung rackets. What's so difficult about that? – I mean they're big enough to use as hula-hoops these days. But live and let live – things change. I mean it was always difficult to hit a backhand so why not make the racket as big as a shed door, and then you don't have to bother with a back-swing, and you can hold it with both hands, and what's wrong with grunting to put your opponent off? No, nothing wrong with the modern game at all...

No.5) Animals, Birds and Insects.

You see it written down all the time, as though the word 'animal' refers to some distinct type of creature, quite separate from birds and insects. I think it must originate from biblical times when animals were described as 'beasts' or 'beasts of the field' to distinguish them from 'birds of the air'. And insects came in 'plagues'.

The animal kingdom is not just about warm blood, four legs and wide eyes. It includes fish, worms, barnacles, and other cold-blooded non-furry creatures. It may not make the logo of the World Wide Fund for Nature, but from a biologist's standpoint, a parasitic tapeworm is just as much an animal as is a giant panda.

No.6) The BBC Weather Map.

I'll need some time just to compose myself here...

[No dear, I'm not shouting at the telly – just relaxing and breathing deeply...]

If you doubt how much we are brainwashed by regular exposure to TV images, ask someone to draw a map of Britain, and afterwards check it with an atlas. Most of us will be surprised to see just how big the landmass is north of the border. But then I suppose the population of Scotland is relatively small compared with southern England, and it really is an impressive piece of computer graphics to project the map of the British Isles as if viewed from a hot-air balloon anchored somewhere over Tunisia. I'm keeping quite calm about this... I must breathe more slowly... nearly at the end of the list.

OK, I'm ready... breathe in...

No.7) That annoying dent in the car door.

Pah!... It hardly seems noticeable now, after getting all that off my chest... Even so, and just as a precautionary measure, I might try parking behind the wheely-bin next year.

FALSE EXPECTATIONS AND
THE FIRST SIGNS OF SPRING

*Exploring the psychology of expectation, the pitfalls of
being an expert, and the search for the first flowers of spring*

Janet answered the phone the other day. It was 6.30pm. Just about to serve dinner.

At this point it's important to point out that the voice on the line had a foreign accent and we had already been pestered earlier in the day by numerous calls from Delhi about surveys 'that will only take a few moments':

"Hello, sorry to be bothering you so late in the evening..."

" Look, this is most inconvenient. We are just about to have a meal. It's out of office hours and no – we don't want to take part in a survey of what we bought last week in a supermarket and how did you get our phone number anyway seeing as we are ex-directory? We're fed up with all this cold-calling and I'm putting the phone down right now."

Actually she didn't say anything like that at all. What she really said was:

"That's alright, how can I help you?" – which was just as well really, for the voice on the line was about to ask:

"Do you have a double room available for the 10th of June?"

Expectations can be misleading.

We see what we expect to see. Take wildlife. I would take people bird watching to a place where I would expect to see a wren:

"You can tell it's a wren," I would say. " The song has a series of phrases with a distinct trill at the end."

A robin begins to sing:

"What's that?" someone asks.

"A wren," I would say with total confidence, without even bothering to look.

And then the robin would appear, and imitate the wren again. I hate that robin.

The problem with being an 'expert' is that everyone expects you to know everything and believes you when you make your pronouncements, and before too long you start believing in your own infallibility. Someone asked me the other day if they should clear-out the old nest material from a blue-tit nest box before this year's birds return. I automatically found myself giving an answer: "No – just leave the old material inside and it will be reused." You see what I mean? I hadn't a clue but I found myself giving the answer with total certainty. The only safeguard is to have a long-suffering wife on hand ready to hit you with a 'rubber hammer' whenever the occasion demands.

We are now into March and winter is supposed to be almost over. The spring equinox is on or around the 21st of March. After that date, the sun is above the horizon for longer than it is below. But there is conflict between the amount of sunlight we receive and the sea temperature which is approaching its coldest this month. The sea has an over-riding effect on the onset of the seasons. Mid-summer is officially the 21st of June, but the hot summer temperatures don't usually arrive until July and August, in keeping with the temperature of the surrounding sea. In fact, the maximum sea temperature around Skye is not reached until September.

For the moment though, we can enjoy the spring. Take a walk on the croft just now and you will find the yellow flowers of lesser celandine. Walk to the cliff edge where there are Jurassic sediments and you see primroses and the first signs of early purple orchids. But for me, the flower that really signals the start of spring is the saxifrage that grows on that fertile rock face, out of reach of sheep, facing north, often in a gully, and often with a smattering of snow. *Saxifraga oppositifolia* is the Latin. Its flowers are deep purple, hence the common name: purple saxifrage.

Saxifrage means 'stone breaker'. The plant is usually found in gullies or rock clefts, with roots penetrating cracks and so eventually helping to break up the surface. Purple saxifrage is found on base-rich rock. It absorbs lime and excretes the excess through pores at the leaf tip, often giving the leaf edge a frosted, crystalline appearance.

Purple saxifrage is used as a time-keeper by the Inuit. When the plant is in flower, it tells them that the reindeer herds are in calf. The clock is remarkably accurate and is set by sunlight rather than temperature. Many other plant clocks are affected by temperature and are responding to global warming by flowering earlier – but good old purple saxifrage keeps true time, and stands out as a constant in a changing world.

The frogs are spawning around the garden. A walk across the top park reveals blobs of translucent jelly scattered over the grass. This is all that is left of the frog – the contents of the oviduct that were discarded by the buzzard and the crow. The unfertilised eggs are coated in albumen, a protein that swells up and becomes sticky in contact with water. Perhaps the gelatinous nature makes it unpalatable and so it is discarded by the predator. Recently, in south Skye, a buzzard has been seen eating toads – apparently 'warts and all' – which is unusual as most animals that eat toads will leave the skin behind because of the poisons they contain.

Male blackbirds are beginning to fine-tune their songs. I heard one singing at five o'clock this morning. Who needs an alarm clock! The call will get earlier as the mornings get lighter. The tune will also change as the season progresses. It is often assumed that it is the male bird that does all the singing but research shows that female singing has been overlooked. In a recent study of 109 European songbirds, only eight species had females that did not sing.

The neighbour's ducks have been happy this past week. Lots of wet grass to search for errant slugs. Sometimes they make their way down to the freshwater loch at the foot of the croft. It reminds me of an incident a few years ago. A minibus stopped outside the house and out poured a group of keen birdwatchers with their leader. Tripods were quickly erected along the roadside and binoculars rested on top of the car roof – all focused on the loch surface. There was lots of excitement and puzzlement as bird books were hastily consulted: "Passage migrants?"... "First winter in moult?"... "Males in eclipse?"

I hadn't the heart to tell them it was Arabella and Jemima.

Evolution and Darwin's Legacy

SHARING A SHELF WITH A SEA SQUIRT

A closer look at the Hemichordates:
the forgotten ancestor on the sea shore

Finding your way around biology is a bit like being in a supermarket. The snails are in the 'Soft Body' section, crabs in 'Jointed Legs', whilst earthworms are on display in 'Rings'.

It all works well until you want to find animals that possess a backbone – what zoologists call vertebrates. I imagine the smiling assistant telling me to go along the top row: "Past the Protozoa and the processed peas, and when you get to the starfish, turn left."

And so I follow directions… and suddenly – success! The shelves are clearly labelled: 'Animals with Backbones' – full of fish, birds and mammals… but alongside, there is an intruder, a blob of slime called a tunicate. Surely this can't be right?

Take any basic textbook on zoology and you find animals split into vertebrates and invertebrates: those with and those without backbones. But what of the tunicates, or sea squirts as they are sometimes called? Where do they belong? Surely they don't possess a backbone?

The larval stage of a sea squirt looks a bit like a tadpole, with a mouth and gill slits at the front end, and a rolled-up tube of nerves down its back. The spine takes the form of a stiff rod of cartilage called a notochord. Because of this they are classified as Chordates.

The supermarket got it right after all. They put these blobs of jelly on the same shelf as *Homo sapiens*. As vertebrates, we belong in the same biological phylum – the Chordates.

What would Victorian anti-Darwinians have made of all this? …

"Might I enquire if the gentleman who believes in evolution is descended from a blob of jelly on his grandmother's or his grandfather's side?"

To which Darwin's bulldog would no doubt have proclaimed his preference for the jelly as an ancestor rather than someone who subverts the evidence to make fun of their opponent.

(This debate actually took place in 1860 at the British Association meeting at Oxford, where the Bishop of Oxford clashed with Darwin's friend, Thomas Henry Huxley. But instead of infering that Huxley's grandparents were tunicates, the bishop had asked whether he was descended from an ape on his grandmother's or grandfather's side.)

Sea squirts are really quite beautiful. Take a walk down the shore at low tide. On the rocks amongst the kelp lives a colonial form by the name *Botryllus schlosseri*, the star sea squirt. The stars are individuals with separate 'mouths' that have come together in an all-enclosing mass of jelly to share a communal 'bottom'. Put more scientifically: they have retained their own inhalant openings but share a central exhalent siphon.

These creatures are almost always passed by. They are unlike anything else to be found on the shore. Everyone is familiar with the likes of crabs, whelks and anemones, but these chordate things have escaped the popular notion of shore life.

Individual sea squirts have two openings on top of a jelly-like sac. If you pick them up, their bodies contract and squirt water at you. They have a heart with two pacemakers – one at each end – which pump blood first in one direction and then the other. The blood may contain orange, green or blue pigments which give the body a range of colours that can vary from day to day.

To see them at their best, you need to watch them under water when these unspeakable blobs of slime become transformed into beautiful ballerinas with transparent tunics and shimmering eye-spots. Fantastic!

One of the most exquisite is *Ciona intestinalis*. The swollen tunic has a see-through underskirt with hundreds of parallel slits that are equivalent to the gill slits in a basking shark. Water is sucked in through one siphon and then gets filtered through the slits before being forced out through a second siphon.

Is there a more beautiful object on the sea bed? Like peering through a tube of fine glass, you can see the contents on display: the thin bunches of muscle fibres running along its full length and linked by a circular collar; the bright orange spots of pigment around the siphons, once thought to be sensitive to light – but now an experimental scientist has disproved this and messed-up what was a nice simple explanation. (That's the trouble with science – it keeps questioning things and complicating the issue.) And then there is that incredible colour within the tunic – due to vanadium pigments in the blood – a faint green turning to metallic blue. Astonishing!

Look closely. Deep within – a tantalising glimpse of the endostyle – a bright glowing rod full of iodine, seen through the opening of the dorsal siphon. Here is where a sticky mucus is produced that is wafted upwards and then backwards into the stomach on masses of waving hairs, ready to trap fine food particles that are constantly being drawn into the huge perforated throat. It could be straight out of science fiction. In fact I'm sure I saw something like it in *Star Trek*: Series One; Episode Three. Wasn't it called 'The Hand of Apollo'?

This creature hasn't changed in millions of years. Its tadpole-like larva ensures dispersal over new areas of seabed. But then the adult just settles down to a perfectly-adapted sessile life, going nowhere. There is no need to go anywhere. Food comes in; no need to chase it. No need to go swimming or crawling about on land. No need to develop its gill slits into jaws or to have arms and legs.

Like the fishes, chimpanzees and other Chordates, the sea squirts are perfectly adapted to their own particular environment. They are successful creatures in their own right, not stepping stones to some 'higher' form of life. We share the same phylum: the same shelf space. They are our contemporaries, not living examples of our ancestors.

NATURE RED IN BEAK AND CLAW

An unsentimental view of nature from a Darwinian perspective, recalling the author's observations of birdlife in Skye

If we are to believe Charles Darwin, nature is all about competition: the struggle for existence and the survival of the fittest. It is the 'war of all against all'. And giving animals names and going "Ah!" and "Ooh!" and "Don't they look pretty!" is just deluding ourselves. "Oh look, Percy has just gouged Philip's eye out!"

Pretty robin redbreast sings his song. He's not singing to make pretty music that he listens to and enjoys like someone singing in the bath. It's a war cry! And woe-betide any other adult male that pokes its beak into his territory. Woe-betide even a bunch of red feathers that happened to be introduced on a twig by David Lack, the English ethologist, in 1939 to examine how a male robin would react. As it happened, the cheery red robin tore the bunch of red feathers to pieces!

Take the chickens for example: that's where the terms 'hen-pecked' and 'pecking order' comes from. Introduce some young pullets into an established group and they all gang-up on the new ones, pecking the comb and neck, even drawing blood. You could say they were all right-wing, aggressive individuals; no such thing as society; (Where did I hear that before?) no thought of caring for the weak – just greed and get all the layers' pellets you can before they are gone.

And after feeding them in the morning, I would look over the fence and compare them with our neighbour's ducks – yes, the same Arabella and Jemima – and I would say, in true Bill Oddie style: "Ah, now look how they all look after each other. Look how the drake keeps them all together and makes sure that no-one is left behind."

That's care. That's looking after those that can't keep up. No hen-pecking here. No right-wing 'look-after-number-one'. No 'me-first'. How I admired those ducks: real socialist, left wing, caring society members... and then the young drakes matured and all this socialist cant was seen for what it was.

Caring drakes? Rubbish! It was all about propagating their own genes. What the top drake was doing was making sure the young drakes didn't get a look-in, and mate with members of his harem; not just mate but rape the females in his charge. Ducks are no better than hens and in some respects they are worse – male ducks constantly try and rape female ducks.

The battle of the sexes has been going on so long in the evolution of this group, the Anatidae, that female ducks have evolved a defence against rape. To avert unwanted advances, spiral muscles inside their vagina twist in the opposite direction to the spiral penis of the drake and so make penetration difficult. We weren't taught that in school biology!

And so it was with some relief that I got away from these domestic fowl with their domestic problems and took a walk along the beach... It was on the north-west coast of Raasay that I spotted the carcass of a bird high up on the shore. It hadn't been washed up by the sea and there were no signs of disease. But it had one unusual feature – there were notches cut into the edge of the sternum. The smooth sickle of the breastbone now looked like a jagged saw. What could have caused such damage?

These were the classic signs of a peregrine attack. The predator plucks the best meat and discards the rest, taking the main flight muscles that are

Victim of a peregrine attack. The notches on the breastbone
show where the falcon's beak has torn away the pectoral muscle

attached to the breastbone. All that remains are the tell-tale notches left by
the peregrine's beak.

I remember a time I was in the garden, digging. I heard a crack like a gun-
shot, and a pigeon exploded above my head in a cloud of feathers. I rushed
across to check what had happened and found a peregrine in characteristic
pose, 'mantling' or standing with its wings part open, covering the bird it
had just killed. The peregrine flew off. I backed away and returned some
hours later, but the remains had gone.

On thinking back, I marvelled at the sheer efficiency of that kill, how
the pigeon had been struck dead, above a patch of wild rose that could
have torn into the peregrine's wings had it misjudged the height. After a
dive of 100mph, it had pulled-out perfectly, barely 20 feet above the
ground.

We have ambivalent views about such aggression. The peregrine is regarded as a noble bird. We are in awe of its agility and raw power and marvel at the speeds it can reach in a dive. The highlight of a birdwatcher's year would have been to see it knock that pigeon out of the sky. But then in the same breath, we curse the crow for stealing eggs, and scorn the skua for harrying kittiwakes.

Here are two observations. First, a golden eagle was flying on a horizontal path towards an approaching fulmar. The two birds suddenly became one as the eagle simply plucked the fulmar out of the air, without any drop in height or change in speed or direction. Effortless superiority! Fantastic!

Second observation: A great black-backed gull attacked an adult shag on the sea surface, holding it by the neck with its beak, forcing its head under water to try and drown it. The struggle was unrelenting. And then after 20 minutes, the shag escaped. Hooray!

The birds don't cheer. The hunter is simply trying to find food. The hunted is itself hunting its own food. Nature just gets on with it. There are no judgements of what is noble or cruel, only those added by the human observer.

LOWER THAN THE ANGELS: HIGHER THAN THE ANIMALS?

A philosophical finalé on the nature of altruism in man and animals

I've been chewing over what to write about this week. Nothing much happening outside – just wind and rain followed by more wind and more rain. So why not look inside? Warning! If you are looking for a list of birds visiting the garden or a record of the first spring flowers, I'm sorry to have to disappoint you. And so if you don't want to hear some manic biologist ranting on about some abstract philosophical bee in his bonnet, then turn away now...

[Janet says she's fed up with all this self-indulgence, and she's off to Morocco next week.]

Every now and then, you come across some really big questions: The origin of the Universe? How did life begin? Do we have free will? But on a day-to-day level, there is no bigger question than that posed by altruism, or the lack of it. Altruism comes from *alteri*, the Latin word for 'others' – putting others before self. We take it for granted that it exists.

But let's cut through all the sentiment straight to the biology. J.B.S. Haldane, the English biologist was drinking with friends in a bar. They were talking about sacrificing their lives for others. Haldane reputedly took out an envelope from his pocket on which he scribbled a quick calculation and then proclaimed: "I will lay down my life for two brothers or eight cousins!" What did he mean?

Biologists call it 'kin selection'. In humans – brothers and sisters share half their genes (cousins share one eighth). We try to preserve our own genes. In ants and bees where members of a colony are much more closely related, the workers will fling themselves at an invader and sacrifice their lives automatically – even for just one sister.

Are we then to reduce self-sacrifice to mere mathematics?

In the peacock, the male risks his life by carrying about this enormous tail fan to attract females. It's a costly strategy, making the bird less agile and prone to attack by predators. In the Arabian babbler, *Turdoides squamiceps*, the social rank and hence the chance of finding a mate increases the more a bird is seen to help others in the flock, even when members of the flock are unrelated. The top bird is the one that shows the most selfless behaviour. Like the peacock's tail, this is a costly strategy, but it works if the payer attracts more mates: anyone who is able to sacrifice valuable resources or spend time helping others must be fit and worth sharing their genes with! Biologists call this 'signalling'.

But is this altruism? I sacrifice myself because I increase the chance of passing on more of my genes?

In the 1960s, there was huge excitement when biologists discovered a mathematical game called the Prisoner's Dilemma. Each player has two choices: cooperate or defect. Each player chooses without knowing what the other will do. Defection always pays more than cooperation. But the rewards are arranged to create a dilemma: if both players act selfishly and defect, they both do worse than if they had cooperated. After a few games, both players learn to cooperate. Biologists call this 'reciprocal altruism'.

Richard Dawkins, the evolutionary biologist (the one people love to hate) found real hope in this. Cooperation can bring rewards. If we are able to remember past events and have an eye on the future, then cooperation can spread quite naturally through a population. In Dawkins' own words: "We have the power to defy the selfish genes..." For many biologists this is the nearest we can hope to get to altruistic behaviour: tit for tat, you scratch my back, to give and count the cost.

All three types of altruism – kin selection, signalling and reciprocal altruism – all depend on getting something in return. The pure ideal of giving at your own expense is undermined. In order to separate-out this purer unconditional version, some (including Dawkins) have used the tautological term 'disinterested altruism'. This implies that what we have been describing so far has been 'interested altruism' – behaviour that is thinking of itself and of a future reward.

Sorry to sound such a pessimistic note, but that's the message from biology. This is so depressing, and the weather isn't getting any better either.

Isn't there a 'nice' side to nature? Something pleasant to lift the spirits? Animals cooperating unconditionally? What of limpets helping their neighbours by clearing the rocks of green algae? This helps the larvae of barnacles and other creatures to settle on bare surfaces. Their importance can be seen after an oil slick, when limpets disappear. As the oil gradually disperses, the first life to return to the shore is often the green seaweeds. The remaining shore life finds it difficult to return without the helping hand of the missing limpets. But of course, a simple creature like a limpet isn't conscious of this act of benevolence.

But what of more complex animals? Sheep – now they give themselves up selflessly to suckling their lambs... but then the mother is only looking after its own (unless it is fooled by dressing an orphan with the skin of its own dead lamb). Eider ducks provide a different story: a large group of young are often looked after with the help of non-breeding adults in a crèche – but then these adults are thought to be related (maiden aunts) and so cooperation is once again explained by kin selection.

It all portrays a rather mechanistic view of the higher sentiments. It seems we are reducing them to the expression of selfish genes or the heartless calculation of consequences. Birds lay their eggs, and the more time they invest in their young, the less likely they are to desert the nest. 'Invest': What am I saying? That's a financial term that implies a reward!

More and more words are being imported into biology from economics. How long before we talk of 'the free market' when describing competition at a nesting colony? Before 'trickle-down' limpets? I heard a biologist the other week describe a wildlife survey as an 'audit'. Has it started already?

Perhaps the business metaphor *is* appropriate. Darwin, after all, was aware of the economic ideas of the Scottish Enlightenment – how the struggle of individuals for their own benefits leads to an ordered economy. One of the books he took with him on the Beagle voyage was Dugald Stewart's *On the Life and Writing of Adam Smith*. Laissez-faire economics could easily have been transferred into Darwin's theory of natural selection. (Stephen Jay Gould discusses this at length in his collection of essays: *The Panda's Thumb*.)

But to return to altruism. Philosophers have argued for centuries over whether or not we are naturally selfish or benevolent. If we are to believe Darwin, life is based on survival of the fittest and we are hardwired with a program called 'preserve self'. That's the grain of nature. Perhaps the really big question is whether a wise ape called *Homo sapiens* can choose to go *against* the grain and, in Dawkins' own words, "cultivate and nurture pure, disinterested altruism".

[… Sorry dear, what was that about Morocco?]

INDEX